Childcraft

The How and Why Library

Volume 1

Once Upon a Time

World Book, Inc.

a Scott Fetzer company

Chicago London Sydney Toronto

Acknowledgments

The publishers of Childcraft—The How and Why Library gratefully acknowledge the courtesy of the following publishers,
agents, authors, and artists who have granted permission to use
copyrighted material in this book. Any errors or omissions are
unintentional and the publisher will be happy to make any necessary corrections in future printings. Full illustration acknowl-
edgments for this volume appear on page 312.

Atheneum Publishers, Inc.: N. M. Bodecker, "My Little Dad,"
"Three Little Guinea Pigs," "Who Is Knocking?" from It's
Raining Said John Twaining. (A Margaret K. McElderry Book.)
Copyright © 1973 by N. M. Bodecker. Reprinted with the per-
mission of Atheneum Publishers. Lilian Moore, "Snowy Morn-
ing" from I Thought I Heard the City. Copyright © 1969 by
Lilian Moore. Reprinted with the permission of Atheneum Pub-
lishers.
Bradbury Press, Inc.: The Bunyip of Berkeley's Creek, story by
Jenny Wagner, pictures by Ron Brooks, first published by
Longman Young Books/Childerset Pty Ltd., 1973. Copyright
© 1973 by Ron Brooks and Childerset Pty Ltd. Reprinted with
permission of Bradbury Press, Inc., Scarsdale, N.Y. 10583,
and Penguin Books Ltd.
Marchette Chute: "Dogs" and "My Dog" from Around and
About by Marchette Chute, copyright 1957. Reprinted by per-
mission of the author.
Doubleday & Company, Inc.: "Rosa-Too-Little," complete text
from Rosa-Too-Little by Sue Felt. Copyright 1950 by Sue Felt
Kerr. Reprinted by permission of Doubleday & Company, Inc.
"Best Game the Fairies Play," from Fairies and Chimneys by
Rose Fyleman. Copyright 1918, 1920 by Scott Doran Co. Re-
printed by permission of Doubleday & Company, Inc., and The
Society of Authors as the literary representative of the Estate
of Rose Fyleman. "Good Night" and "Mice," from Fifty-One
New Nursery Rhymes by Rose Fyleman. Copyright 1932 by
Doubleday & Company, Inc. Reprinted by permission of the
publisher, and The Society of Authors as the literary
representative of the Estate of Rose Fyleman. "How the Camel
Got His Hump" from Just So Stories by Rudyard Kipling.
Copyright 1912 by Rudyard Kipling. Reprinted by permission
of Doubleday & Company, Inc., and A. P. Watt Ltd. for The Na-
tional Trust and Macmillan London Limited. "The Velveteen
Rabbit," excerpt from The Velveteen Rabbit by Margery Williams. Reprinted by permission of Doubleday, Inc., and William
Heinemann Limited.
E. P. Dutton, Inc.: Why Mosquitoes Buzz in People's Ears by
Verna Aardema. Text from Why Mosquitoes Buzz in People's
Ears by Verna Aardema. Reprinted by permission of the publisher, Dial Books for Young Readers, a Division of E. P. Dutton, and Curtis Brown, Ltd. "Stars" from Stories to Begin On
by Rhoda Bacmeister. Copyright 1940 by E. P. Dutton, Inc.;
renewed 1968 by Rhoda Bacmeister. Reproduced by permission of the publisher. "The Little Elfman" by John Kendrick
Bangs, from the St. Nicholas Book of Verse. Copyright 1923,
1951 by John Kendrick Bangs. Reprinted by permission of the
publisher. "Jump or Jiggle" by Evelyn Beyer, from Another
Here and Now Storybook by Lucy Sprague Mitchell. Copyright
1937 by E. P. Dutton, Inc.; renewed 1965 by Lucy Sprague

Mitchell. Reproduced by permission of the publisher. "My
Teddy Bear" from Rhymes About Us by Marchette Chute,
copyright © 1974 by Marchette Chute. Reprinted by permission of the publisher, E. P. Dutton, Inc. "Furry Bear" from Now
We Are Six by A. A. Milne, copyright 1927 by E. P. Dutton,
Inc., renewed 1955 by A. A. Milne. Reprinted by permission of
the publisher; Methuen Children's Books; and the Canadian
Publishers, McClelland and Stewart Limited, Toronto. "Hoppity" from When We Were Very Young by A. A. Milne, copy-
right 1924 by E. P. Dutton, Inc., renewed 1952 by A. A. Milne.
Reproduced by permission of the publisher, and the Canadian
publishers, McClelland and Stewart Limited, Toronto. "Pooh
Goes Visiting" from Winnie-the-Pooh by A. A. Milne, illustrated
by Ernest H. Shepard, copyright 1926 by E. P. Dutton & Co.,
Inc., renewed 1954 by A. A. Milne. Reprinted by permission of
E. P. Dutton, Inc., Methuen Children's Books, and the Cana-
dian Publishers, McClelland and Stewart Limited, Toronto.
Coloring of illustrations by Hilda Scott, copyright © 1974 by
E. P. Dutton & Co., Inc., and reproduced with their permission.
Shepard color illustration from The World of Pooh by A. A.
Milne, copyright © 1975 by E. P. Dutton, Inc. Reproduced by
permission of E. P. Dutton, Inc., Curtis Brown, Ltd., London,
and the Canadian Publishers, McClelland and Stewart Limited,
Toronto. "The House of the Mouse" by Lucy Sprague Mitch-
ell, from Another Here and Now Storybook by Lucy Sprague
Mitchell. Copyright 1937 by E. P. Dutton, Inc.; renewed 1965
by Lucy Sprague Mitchell. Reproduced by permission of the
publisher.
Ivy O. Eastwick: "Moon-in-Water," courtesy Ivy O. Eastwick.
Farrar, Straus & Giroux, Inc.: "Mommies" from Spin a Soft
Black Song by Nikki Giovanni. Copyright © 1971 by Nikki
Giovanni. Reprinted by permission of Hill and Wang, a division
of Farrar, Straus and Giroux, Inc.
Aileen Fisher: "After a Bath" from Inside a Little House and
"Otherwise" from Coffee-Pot Face.
Harper & Row, Publishers, Inc.: "The Mitten Song" and "My
Zipper Suit" from A Pocketful of Rhymes by Marie Louise
Allen, copyright 1939 by Harper & Row, Publishers, Inc.
"Cynthia in the Snow" from Bronzeville Boys and Girls by
Gwendolyn Brooks. Copyright © 1956 by Gwendolyn Brooks
Blakely. "The Purple Cow" by Gelett Burgess from The Bur-
gess Book of Nonsense published by J. B. Lippincott. "The
Sheep with the Wooden Collar" from Sashes Red and Blue by
Natalie Savage Carlson, copyright © 1956 by Natalie Savage
Carlson. All reprinted by permission of Harper & Row, Publish-
ers, Inc. "A Kitten," "Moon-Come-Out," and "Mrs. Peck-Pi-
geon" from Eleanor Farjeon's Poems for Children (J. B.
Lippincott Company); copyright 1933, 1961 by Eleanor Far-
jeon. Reprinted by permission of Harper & Row Publishers,
Inc., and Harold Ober Associates Inc. "Go to Sleep," "Here Is
the Family," and "It's Blowing, It's Snowing" from Mother
Goose Abroad. Nursery Rhymes collected by Nicholas Tucker
(Thomas Y. Crowell Company). Copyright © 1974 by Nicholas
Tucker. Reprinted by permission of Harper & Row, Publishers,
Inc., and Hamish Hamilton Limited. "I Keep Three Wishes
Ready" from All Through the Year by Annette Wynne, copy-
right 1932 by Annette Wynne (J. B. Lippincott Company). Re-
printed by permission of Harper & Row, Publishers, Inc.

Volume 1

Once Upon a Time

Contents

Preface

Childcraft was first published in 1934. Since then it has undergone substantial revision several times. This edition is a 15-volume resource library designed especially for preschool and primary-grade children and for the older child who needs high-interest, easy-to-read materials. *Childcraft* also serves as a resource for parents, teachers, and librarians.

Outstanding educational and child guidance specialists serve on the Childcraft Editorial Advisory Board. This group works with the editors and artists in selecting and preparing the contents of these volumes. *Childcraft* concentrates on broad areas of children's interests that have been identified through research and direct observation of children.

In addition, *Childcraft* relates to broad areas of the school curriculum. Volumes 1, 2, and 3 relate to literature and language arts; Volumes 4, 5, 6, and 7 to science, natural history, and technology; Volumes 8, 9, and 10 to social studies; Volumes 11 and 12 to creative activities, the arts, and communication; Volume 13 to mathematics; and Volume 14 to self-understanding. Of course, Volume 15 is designed primarily to serve parents and teachers.

Throughout *Childcraft*, the easy-to-read text is combined with colorful, appealing illustrations that make the material not only fun to read, but also fun to look at. Nearly every graphic technique appears somewhere in *Childcraft*. The illustrators include many of the world's top-ranking artists and photographers. Among the many outstanding artists are winners of the Caldecott Medal, presented annually by the Association for Library Service to Children of the American Library Association "for the most distinguished American picture book for children"; the Kate Greenaway Medal, awarded by the Library Association (British) for distinguished work in the illustration of children's books; and, since 1966, the Hans Christian Andersen International Children's Book Medal honoring an illustrator for "an important international contribution to juvenile literature."

Childcraft is designed to encourage the young child to open doors to life and learning. The volumes also help start the child on a lifelong adventure of enrichment through books. For more information on using *Childcraft* effectively, see Volume 15.

The Editors and Artists

Reading to Your Child

The day is drawing to a close. The light is golden, the shadows long. A small someone, bathed and ready for bed, curls up on your lap. You reach for a book.

"Once upon a time there was a Mother Pig with three Little Pigs. . . ." Small hands push at the page, wanting the story to move along. You skip parts of the tale, stopping at pictures. "See the first little pig?" you ask. A finger touches the page. "I see a wolf," you say. "Where's that old wolf?" The finger rests on the wolf.

You leapfrog through the story, pointing out the house of sticks, the house of bricks. But you never miss the wonderful refrain, "Little Pig, Little Pig, let me come in." "No, no, not by the hair on my chinny chin chin."

Are you actually "reading" to your child? You certainly are. You are quite sensibly adapting the material to the understanding of your listener. As your child grows, the short span of attention typical of the young child will lengthen. You will read more and more of the story until, in time, you can read it all. After that, make no mistake, you will not be able to skip one word of a much-loved tale.

Why Should I Read to My Child?

Reading to your child is a wonderful way to share a close, loving relationship, for it is a time of pleasure for both of you. Your child is fortunate indeed if you read aloud, for he or she is also learning that a book holds a world of wonder and enjoyment.

At the same time, your child is learning that those strange black lines on the page are the source of the words you speak and that someday he or she will be able to read those words. He or she is also discovering that you are reading from left to right and from top to bottom. And think about the pictures your child studies so intently. The realization that the flat apple on the page represents a real, rounded apple he or she can hold is an enormous leap in comprehension.

Story time also provides opportunities to improve vocabulary and develop readiness for reading. Study after study has shown the connection between reading to children and their success in acquiring basic reading skills. So, while you are reading, talk with your child about the story. And answer your child's questions about letters, sounds, and words.

When Should I Start Reading to My Child?

No child is too young to be read to. Many informed educators recommend reading short, simple rhymes to infants only a few weeks old. Your baby may not understand your words, but he or she will enjoy hearing your voice and feeling your loving touch.

A few simple suggestions may prove helpful: If a story has some particular meaning for your child, he or she will often sit still for a far longer time than you might expect. Remember, also, that all children like to go back to the familiar from time to time. This desire is reflected in the poems and stories they choose. There is no "right" or "wrong." There are only your child's interests.

Birth–2: Read the Mother Goose rhymes in this volume. Your baby will respond to the rhythm of the words and the sound of your voice. Play with your child's hands, fingers, or toes as you read "Pat-a-Cake" or "This Little Pig Went to Market." This is fun for your baby and will soon draw smiles. These happy responses establish a pattern for later learning experiences.

Ages 2–3: Continue to read nursery rhymes, but try some of the simple stories in this volume, too. Make good use of the pictures. If necessary, shorten the tales or "read" them in your own words: "Look. Here's the Baby Bear. Here is his bowl of porridge. And here is Goldilocks. She ate the porridge ... all ... up." As you talk or read, point to the characters and objects in the pictures.

Ages 3–5: Now you will be able to read complete stories. Most children in this age group will sit still long enough to hear a short folk tale or fairy tale, such as "The Gingerbread Boy" or "Why the Bear Has a Stumpy Tail." You should also try some of the easy picture book stories in Volume 2, such as *A Kiss for Little Bear* and *Frog and Toad.*

And don't overlook poetry. The stories and poems on pages 154–291 are so arranged that the poems following each story pick up the theme of the story. For example, *Whistle for Willie,* about a small boy who wants to be able to whistle for his dog, is followed by poems about whistling and dogs.

Finally, use the section "Things to Know" in the last part of this volume. Here you will find rhymes about many of the concepts you'll want your child to understand before opening day of kindergarten—the alphabet, numbers from 1 to 10, days of the week, months of the year, colors, and the time of day.

Ages 5–7: Now is the time to look for stories with a more complex turn of plot. *Cinderella* is such a story. So are *Jack and the Beanstalk* and *Why Mosquitoes Buzz in People's Ears.* Stories that are too long to be read at one sitting, such as the excerpts from *Peter Pan* and *Pinocchio,* can be read a few pages at a time. Look for poems, too, that connect with your child's special interests.

Ages 7 and Up: At seven, most children can read easy stories such as those at the front of Volume 2. But this does not mean that you should stop reading aloud to your child. In fact, it is most important that you continue. Reading aloud gives you a chance to whet your child's appetite for some of the great classics for children, such as those toward the end of Volume 2 and in Volume 3.

How to Read Aloud

You don't have to be an actor or actress, or even a great reader, to read to your child. Your child wants your attention and will respond to your love and interest. Even so, anyone can do some simple things to add to the excitement and appeal of a story or poem. Make loud sounds loud, soft sounds soft. Growl when you read the words of the big bad Wolf. Your child will delight in your entry into the world of play.

A Final Word

Before you read any story or poem to your child, read it, or at least skim it, yourself. Ask yourself: Will this interest my child? Will he or she understand what is happening? What might I have to explain? Is this a good bedtime story, or should I read it at some other time?

Which brings up the question: When is the best time to read aloud? *Anytime.* And try to make reading aloud to your child a daily activity. Of course, bedtime is a favorite time because reading a story then helps to end the day on a calm, happy note. It is also a time that daddy can share with his little one. And for working parents, it may be the only time available. Whatever the time, enjoy it. Know that reading to your child is the gift of a lifetime. That gift will become part of your child's bank of memories, one that will be treasured long after childhood has passed.

Nursery Rhymes

Old Mother Goose

Old Mother Goose,
　　When she wanted to wander,
Would ride through the air
　　On a very fine gander.

Mother Goose had a house,
　　'Twas built in a wood,
Where an owl at the door
　　For a sentinel stood.

Bye, Baby Bunting

Bye, baby bunting,
Daddy's gone a-hunting,
Gone to get a rabbit skin
To wrap the baby bunting in.

Hush, Baby, My Doll

Hush, baby, my doll, I pray you don't cry,
And I'll give you some bread and some milk by and by;
Or, perhaps, you like custard, or, maybe, a tart—
Then to either you're welcome, with all my whole heart.

Rock-a-Bye Baby

Rock-a-bye, baby,
  Thy cradle is green,
Father's a nobleman,
  Mother's a queen;
And Betty's a lady,
  And wears a gold ring;
And Johnny's a drummer,
  And drums for the king.

Hush-a-Bye Baby

Hush-a-bye, baby, on the tree top,
When the wind blows the cradle will rock;
When the bough breaks the cradle will fall,
Down will come baby, cradle, and all.

Willow Leaves Murmur
a Chinese nursery rhyme
adapted by Robert Wyndham

Willow leaves murmur, hua-la-la.
Sleep, precious baby, close to mama.
Hua-la-la, baby, smile in your sleep;
You'll have only sweet dreams
While my watch I keep.

Pat-a-Cake

Pat-a-cake, pat-a-cake, baker's man,
Bake me a cake as fast as you can;
Pat it and prick it, and mark it with B,
Put it in the oven for baby and me.

Go to Sleep

a French nursery rhyme
adapted by Nicholas Tucker

Go to sleep,
My dear little brother,
Go to sleep,
Dear brother of mine.
  Papa is a knight
  With armor so bright;
  Mama is a queen,
  In her dresses of green.
Go to sleep,
My dear little brother,
Go to sleep,
Dear brother of mine.

14

Lullaby

by Christina Rossetti

Lullaby, oh, lullaby!
Flowers are closed and lambs are sleeping;
Lullaby, oh, lullaby!
Stars are up, the moon is peeping;
Lullaby, oh, lullaby!
While the birds are silence keeping,
Lullaby, oh, lullaby!
Sleep, my baby, fall a-sleeping,
Lullaby, oh, lullaby!

The Song of the Frog

a Japanese nursery rhyme
adapted by Charlotte B. DeForest

So hushaby, baby, if you'll go to sleep,
I'll give you a pretty red flower to keep.
But if you keep crying, a big ugly frog
Will croak by your side—kerchog! kerchog!

Lullaby to a Naughty Baby

a Venezuelan nursery rhyme
adapted by Joan Gilbert Van Poznak

Lullaby, naughty child,
Your nonsense drives your mother wild.

Lullaby, arrurru,
What can Mama do with you?

Work all day, up all night,
By morning nothing's going right.

Lullaby, arrurru,
What can Mama do with you?

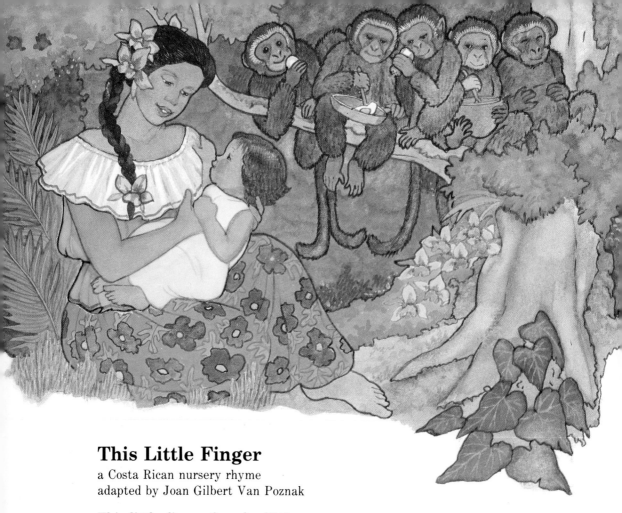

This Little Finger
a Costa Rican nursery rhyme
adapted by Joan Gilbert Van Poznak

This little finger found a little egg,
This little finger cooked it,
This little finger sprinkled salt on it,
This little finger scrambled it,
And this mischievous fat one ate it!

Here Is the Family
a German nursery rhyme
adapted by Nicholas Tucker

This is the father, short and stout,
And this is mother, with children all about.
And this is the brother, tall you see,
And this is the sister with her dolly on her knee.
This is the baby, still to grow,
And here is the family, all in a row.

My Little Dad

a Danish nursery rhyme
adapted by N.M. Bodecker

My little Dad
had five little piggies:
good 'un,
bad 'un,
gay 'un,
sad 'un,
and one little piggie
who was
mad
      mad
         mad!
Five little piggies
had my little Dad.

This Little Cow

a Chinese nursery rhyme
adapted by Robert Wyndham

This little cow eats grass,
This little cow eats hay,
This little cow drinks water,
This little cow runs away,
And *this* little cow does nothing
But lie down all the day.

This Little Pig Went to Market

This little pig went to market,
This little pig stayed at home,
This little pig had roast beef,
This little pig had none,
And this little pig cried, "Wee, wee, wee!"
All the way home.

This Is the Way the Ladies Ride

This is the way the ladies ride,
   Nimble, nimble, nimble, nimble!
This is the way the ladies ride,
   A-nimble, nimble, nimble!

This is the way the gentlemen ride,
   Gallop-a-trot, gallop-a-trot!
This is the way the gentlemen ride,
   Gallop-a-gallop-a-trot!

This is the way the farmers ride,
   Hobbledy-hoy, hobbledy-hoy!
This is the way the farmers ride,
   Hobbledy-hobbledy-hoy!

Ride a Cockhorse

Ride a cockhorse to Banbury Cross,
To see a fine lady upon a white horse;
Rings on her fingers and bells on her toes,
And she shall have music wherever she goes.

To Market, to Market

To market, to market,
To buy a fat pig,
Home again, home again,
Jiggety-jig.

To market, to market,
To buy a fat hog,
Home again, home again,
Jiggety-jog.

To market, to market,
To buy a plum bun,
Home again, home again,
Market is done.

19

Humpty Dumpty

Humpty Dumpty sat on a wall,
Humpty Dumpty had a great fall.
  All the king's horses,
    And all the King's men,
Couldn't put Humpty together again.

Little Miss Muffet

Little Miss Muffet
Sat on a tuffet,
Eating her curds and whey;
There came a big spider,
Who sat down beside her
And frightened Miss Muffet away.

There Was an Old Woman

There was an old woman
  Lived under a hill,
And if she's not gone
  She lives there still.

I Had a Little Nut Tree

I had a little nut tree,
  Nothing would it bear
But a silver nutmeg
  And a golden pear;

The King of Spain's daughter
  Came to visit me,
And all for the sake
  Of my little nut tree.

One Misty, Moisty Morning

One misty, moisty, morning,
When cloudy was the weather,
I chanced to meet an old man
Clothed all in leather;
Clothed all in leather,
With a strap beneath his chin.
How do you do, and how do you do,
And how do you do again?

Sing a Song of Sixpence

Sing a song of sixpence,
  A pocket full of rye;
Four and twenty blackbirds
  Baked in a pie.

When the pie was opened,
  The birds began to sing;
Was not that a dainty dish
  To set before the king?

The king was in his counting-house,
  Counting out his money;
The queen was in the parlor,
  Eating bread and honey.

The maid was in the garden,
  Hanging out the clothes;
There came a little blackbird
  And snapped off her nose.
But there came a Jenny Wren
  And popped it on again.

Jeremiah Obediah

Jeremiah Obediah puffs, puffs, puffs;
When he gets his messages, he snuffs, snuffs, snuffs;
When he goes to school by day, he roars, roars, roars;
And when he goes to bed at night, he snores, snores,
   snores.

Wee Willie Winkie

Wee Willie Winkie
   Runs through the town,
Upstairs and downstairs
   In his nightgown,
Rapping at the window,
   Crying through the lock,
"Are the children in their beds,
   For now it's eight o'clock?"

It's Raining, It's Pouring

It's raining, it's pouring,
The old man's a-snoring.
He went to bed
And bumped his head
And couldn't get up in the morning.

Diddle, Diddle, Dumpling

Diddle, diddle, dumpling, my son John,
Went to bed with his trousers on;
One shoe off, and one shoe on,
Diddle, diddle, dumpling, my son John.

Old King Cole

Old King Cole
Was a merry old soul,
And a merry old soul was he;
He called for his pipe,
And he called for his bowl,
And he called for his fiddlers three.

Every fiddler, he had a fiddle,
And a very fine fiddle had he;
Oh, there's none so rare
As can compare
With King Cole and his fiddlers three.

Polly Put the Kettle On

Polly put the kettle on,
Polly put the kettle on,
Polly put the kettle on,
    We'll all have tea!

Sukey take it off again,
Sukey take it off again,
Sukey take it off again,
    They've all gone away.

Jack Sprat

Jack Sprat could eat no fat,
His wife could eat no lean;
And so between them both, you see,
They licked the platter clean.

Little Tommy Tucker

Little Tommy Tucker
Sings for his supper:
What shall we give him?
White bread and butter.

How shall he cut it
Without any knife?
How shall he marry
Without any wife?

Hot Cross Buns

Hot cross buns!
Hot cross buns!
One a penny, two a penny,
Hot cross buns!
If you have no daughters,
Give them to your sons.
One a penny, two a penny,
Hot cross buns!

Little Jack Horner

Little Jack Horner
Sat in the corner,
Eating a Christmas pie;
He put in his thumb,
And pulled out a plum,
And said, "What a good boy am I!"

The Queen
of Hearts

The Queen of Hearts
She made some tarts,
All on a summer's day;
The Knave of Hearts
He stole the tarts,
And took them clean away.

The King of Hearts
Called for the tarts,
And beat the knave full sore;
The Knave of Hearts
Brought back the tarts,
And vowed he'd steal no more.

What Are Little Boys Made Of?

What are little boys made of?
What are little boys made of?
Frogs and snails, and puppy-dogs' tails,
That's what little boys are made of.

What Are Little Girls Made Of?

What are little girls made of?
What are little girls made of?
Sugar and spice, and all that's nice,
That's what little girls are made of.

Tom, Tom
the Piper's Son

Tom, Tom, the piper's son,
Stole a pig and away he run;
   The pig was eat
   And Tom was beat,
And Tom went howling down the street.

Ding, Dong, Bell

Ding, dong, bell,
Pussy's in the well.
Who put her in?
Little Johnny Green.
Who pulled her out?
Little Tommy Stout.
What a naughty boy was that,
To try to drown poor pussy cat,
Who never did any harm,
And killed the mice in his father's barn.

There Was a Little Girl

There was a little girl, and she had a little curl
Right in the middle of her forehead;
When she was good, she was very, very good,
But when she was bad, she was horrid.

Rub-a-Dub-Dub

Rub-a-dub-dub,
Three men in a tub,
And who do you think they be?
The butcher, the baker,
The candlestick-maker;
Turn 'em out, knaves all three!

Jack and Jill

Jack and Jill went up the hill
   To fetch a pail of water;
Jack fell down and broke his crown,
   And Jill came tumbling after.

Then up Jack got, and home did trot,
   As fast as he could caper,
To old Dame Dob, who patched his nob
   With vinegar and brown paper.

Georgie Porgie

Georgie Porgie, pudding and pie,
Kissed the girls and made them cry;
When the boys came out to play,
Georgie Porgie ran away.

Mary, Mary,
Quite Contrary

Mary, Mary, quite contrary,
　　How does your garden grow?
With silver bells and cockleshells,
　　And pretty maids all in a row.

A Lost Snowflake

a Japanese nursery rhyme
adapted by Charlotte B. DeForest

The snowflakes fell, the first this year.
I caught one on my sleeve—right here!
I thought that we would play all day.
But then it melted—right away!

Two Little Sisters

a Chinese nursery rhyme
adapted by Robert Wyndham

Two little sisters went walking one day,
Partly for exercise, partly for play.
They took with them kites which they wanted to fly,
One a big centipede, one a great butterfly.
Then up in a moment the kites floated high,
Like dragons that seemed to be touching the sky!

My Little Golden Sister

a Chinese nursery rhyme
adapted by Robert Wyndham

My little golden sister
Rides a golden horse so slow;
She'll have to use a golden whip
To make her slow horse go.

A little golden fish
In a golden bowl has she;
And a golden bird is singing
On a golden cherry tree.

A smiling golden Buddha
In a golden temple stands,
With a tiny golden baby
In his gentle golden hands.

It's Blowing, It's Snowing

a Dutch nursery rhyme
adapted by Nicholas Tucker

It's blowing, it's snowing,
    Children are tumbling down.
So tie your cap beneath your chin,
    And run and fetch the washing in.

There Was a Crooked Man

There was a crooked man, and he walked a crooked mile,
He found a crooked sixpence against a crooked stile;
He bought a crooked cat, which caught a crooked mouse,
And they all lived together in a little crooked house.

Peter, Peter, Pumpkin-Eater

Peter, Peter, pumpkin-eater,
Had a wife and couldn't keep her;
He put her in a pumpkin shell,
And there he kept her very well.

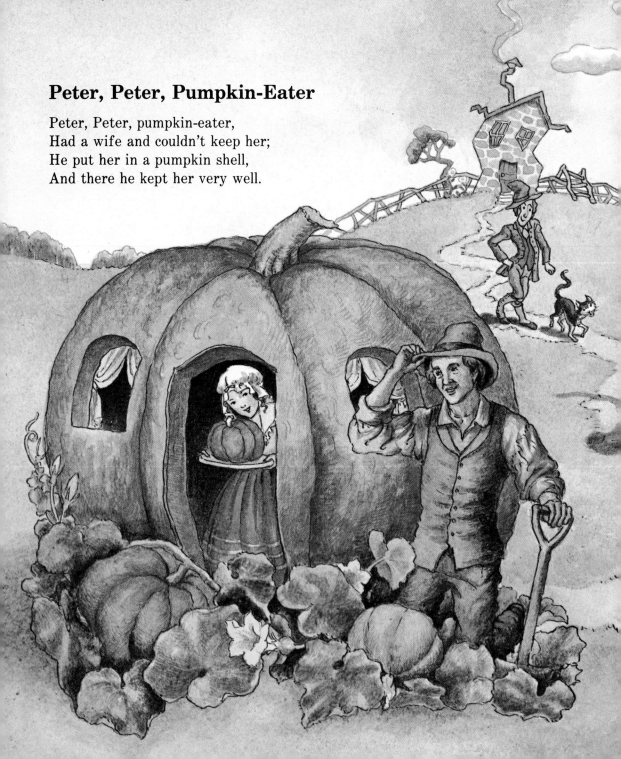

There Was an Old Woman
Who Lived in a Shoe

There was an old woman who lived in a shoe,
She had so many children she didn't know what to do;
She gave them some broth without any bread;
She spanked them all soundly and sent them to bed.

Hey, Diddle, Diddle

Hey, diddle, diddle!
The cat and the fiddle,
The cow jumped over the moon;
The little dog laughed
To see such sport,
And the dish ran away with the spoon.

39

Simple Simon

Simple Simon met a pieman
   Going to the fair;
Says Simple Simon to the pieman,
   "Let me taste your ware."

Says the pieman to Simple Simon,
   "Show me first your penny."
Says Simple Simon to the pieman,
   "Indeed, I have not any."

Simple Simon went a-fishing
   For to catch a whale;
But all the water he had got
   Was in his mother's pail.

He went to catch a dicky-bird,
   And thought he could not fail,
Because he had a pinch of salt
   To put upon its tail.

Three Blind Mice

Three blind mice, see how they run!
They all ran after the farmer's wife,
Who cut off their tails with a carving knife,
Did you ever see such a thing in your life,
   As three blind mice?

Goosey, Goosey Gander

Goosey, goosey gander,
    Whither shall I wander?
Upstairs and downstairs
    And in my lady's chamber.

There I met an old man
    Who would not say his prayers.
I took him by the left leg
    And threw him down the stairs.

Barber, Barber

Barber, barber, shave a pig,
How many hairs will make a wig?
"Four-and-twenty, that's enough."
Give the poor barber a pinch of snuff.

Old Mother Hubbard

Old Mother Hubbard
Went to the cupboard,
To fetch her poor dog a bone,
But when she got there
The cupboard was bare,
And so the poor dog had none.

She went to the baker's
To buy him some bread,
But when she came back
The poor dog was dead.

She went to the undertaker's
To buy him a coffin,
But when she came back
The poor dog was laughing.

She took a clean dish
To get him some tripe,
But when she came back
He was smoking a pipe.

She went to the fruiterer's
To buy him some fruit,
But when she came back
He was playing the flute.

She went to the tailor's
To buy him a coat,
But when she came back
He was riding a goat.

She went to the hatter's
To buy him a hat,
But when she came back
He was feeding the cat.

She went to the barber's
To buy him a wig,
But when she came back
He was dancing a jig.

She went to the cobbler's
To buy him some shoes,
But when she came back
He was reading the news.

The dame made a curtsy,
The dog made a bow.
The dame said, "Your servant."
The dog said, "Bow-wow."

Cock-a-Doodle-Doo

Cock-a-doodle-doo!
My dame has lost her shoe,
My master's lost his fiddlestick,
And knows not what to do!

Cock-a-doodle-doo!
What is my dame to do?
Till master finds his fiddlestick,
She'll dance without her shoe.

Two Cats of Kilkenny

There once were two cats of Kilkenny,
Each thought there was one cat too many;
So they fought and they fit,
And they scratched and they bit,
Till, excepting their nails
And the tips of their tails,
Instead of two cats, there weren't any.

Three Wise Men of Gotham

Three wise men of Gotham,
They went to sea in a bowl,
And if the bowl had been stronger
My song had been longer.

Punch and Judy

Punch and Judy
   Fought for a pie;
Punch gave Judy
   A knock in the eye.
Says Punch to Judy,
   "Will you have any more?"
Says Judy to Punch,
   "My eye is sore."

If All the World Were Paper

If all the world were paper,
And all the sea were ink,
And all the trees were bread and cheese,
What would we have to drink?

Little Boy Blue

Little Boy Blue, come blow your horn,
The sheep's in the meadow, the cow's in the corn;
But where is the boy who looks after the sheep?
He's under a haycock, fast asleep.
Will you wake him? No, not I,
For if I do, he's sure to cry.

Little Bo-Peep

Little Bo-Peep has lost her sheep,
  And can't tell where to find them;
Leave them alone, and they'll come home,
  And bring their tails behind them.

Little Bo-Peep fell fast asleep,
  And dreamt she heard them bleating;
But when she awoke, she found it a joke,
  For they were still all fleeting.

Then up she took her little crook,
  Determined for to find them;
She found them indeed, but it made her heart bleed,
  For they'd left their tails behind them.

It happened one day, as Bo-Peep did stray
  Into a meadow hard by,
There she espied their tails side by side,
  All hung on a tree to dry.

She heaved a sigh, and wiped her eye,
  And over the hillocks went rambling,
And tried what she could, as a shepherdess should,
  To tack again each to its lambkin.

47

I Had a Little Pony

I had a little pony,
    His name was Dapple Gray;
I lent him to a lady
    To ride a mile away.
She whipped him, she slashed him,
    She rode him through the mire;
I would not lend my pony now,
    For all the lady's hire.

Oh Where Has My Little Dog Gone?

Oh where, oh where has my little dog gone?
    Oh where, oh where can he be?
With his ears cut short and his tail cut long,
    Oh where, oh where is he?

Bow, Wow, Wow

Bow, wow, wow,
Whose dog art thou?
Little Tom Tinker's dog,
Bow, wow, wow.

Hickety, Pickety, My Black Hen

Hickety, pickety, my black hen,
She lays eggs for gentlemen;
Gentlemen come every day
To see what my black hen doth lay.
Sometimes nine and sometimes ten,
Hickety, pickety, my black hen.

Baa, Baa, Black Sheep

Baa, Baa, black sheep,
Have you any wool?
Yes sir, yes sir,
Three bags full;

One for my master,
And one for my dame,
And one for the little boy
Who lives down the lane.

49

Mary Had a Little Lamb

by Sarah Josepha Hale

Mary had a little lamb,
   Its fleece was white as snow;
And everywhere that Mary went
   The lamb was sure to go.

It followed her to school one day,
   Which was against the rule;
It made the children laugh and play
   To see a lamb at school.

And so the teacher turned it out,
   But still it lingered near;
And waited patiently about
   Till Mary did appear.

"Why does the lamb love Mary so?"
   The eager children cry;
"Why, Mary loves the lamb, you know,"
   The teacher did reply.

Higglety, Pigglety, Pop

Higglety, pigglety, pop!
The dog has eaten the mop;
  The pig's in a hurry,
  The cat's in a flurry,
Higglety, pigglety, pop!

Pussycat, Pussycat

Pussycat, pussycat, where have you been?
I've been to London to look at the Queen.
Pussycat, pussycat, what did you there?
I frightened a little mouse under her chair.

Three Little Guinea Pigs

a Danish nursery rhyme
adapted by N. M. Bodecker

Three little Guinea pigs
went to see the King.
One brought a rose;
one brought a ring;
one brought a turnip
to give to the King.

Two went back home
neither fatter nor thinner.
One sat on the Queen's lap
and ate the King's dinner.

Who Is Knocking?

a Danish nursery rhyme
adapted by N. M. Bodecker

Who is knocking,
knock, knock, knock?
Charlie, Charlie,
chuck, chuck, chuck!
Who will open
up, up, up?
Peter, Peter,
hop, hop, hop!

Froggie, Froggie

a Chinese nursery rhyme
adapted by Robert Wyndham

Froggie, froggie,
Hoppity-hop!
When you get to the sea
You do not stop.

Plop!

The Prancing Pony

a Japanese nursery rhyme
adapted by Charlotte B. DeForest

Your prancing, dancing pony—
   Oh, please don't tie him here.
This cherry tree's in blossom—
   Oh, dear, dear, dear!

He'll prance and dance and whinny,
   He'll neigh and stamp and call,
And down the soft, pink blossoms
   Will fall, fall, fall!

Three Little Kittens

Three little kittens they lost their mittens,
   And they began to cry,
   "Oh, mother dear,
   We sadly fear
   Our mittens we have lost."

"What! lost your mittens, you naughty kittens!
   Then you shall have no pie."
   "Mee-ow, mee-ow, mee-ow."
   "No, you shall have no pie."

The three little kittens they found their mittens,
   And they began to cry,
   "Oh, mother dear,
   See here, see here,
   Our mittens we have found!"

"Put on your mittens, you silly kittens,
   And you shall have some pie."
   "Purr-r, purr-r, purr-r,
   Oh, let us have some pie."

The three little kittens put on their mittens,
 And soon ate up the pie.
 "Oh, mother dear,
 We greatly fear
 Our mittens we have soiled."

"What! soiled your mittens, you naughty kittens!"
 Then they began to sigh,
 "Mee-ow, mee-ow, mee-ow."
 Then they began to sigh.

The three little kittens they washed their mittens,
 And hung them out to dry;
 "Oh! mother dear,
 Do you not hear,
 Our mittens we have washed?"

"What! washed your mittens, then you're good kittens,
 But I smell a rat close by."
 "Mee-ow, mee-ow, mee-ow.
 We smell a rat close by."

The Wise Old Owl

A wise old owl lived in an oak;
The more he saw the less he spoke;
The less he spoke the more he heard.
Why can't we all be like that wise old bird?

Once I Saw a Little Bird

Once I saw a little bird
   Come hop, hop, hop,
I cried, "Little bird,
   Will you stop, stop, stop?"

I was going to the window
   To say, "How do you do?"
But he shook his little tail
   And away he flew.

Little Robin Redbreast

Little Robin Redbreast sat upon a tree,
Up went Pussycat, and down went he;
Down came Pussy, and away Robin ran;
Says little Robin Redbreast, "Catch me if you can."

Little Robin Redbreast jumped upon a wall,
Pussycat jumped after him, and almost got a fall;
Little Robin chirped and sang, and what did Pussy say?
Pussycat said, "Mew," and Robin jumped away.

The North Wind Doth Blow

The north wind doth blow,
And we shall have snow,
And what will poor Robin do then?
    Poor thing!
He'll sit in a barn,
And keep himself warm,
And hide his head under his wing.
    Poor thing!

Rain, Rain

Rain, rain, go away,
Come again another day.

Doctor Foster

Doctor Foster went to Gloucester
In a shower of rain;
He stepped in a puddle,
Right up to his middle,
And never went there again.

How Many Miles
To Babylon?

How many miles to Babylon?
Three score miles and ten.
Can I get there by candlelight?
Yes, and back again.
If your heels are nimble and light,
You may get there by candlelight.

Rain on the
Green Grass

Rain on the green grass,
Rain on the tree,
Rain on the housetop,
But not on me.

The House That Jack Built

This is the house that Jack built.

This is the malt
That lay in the house that Jack built.

This is the rat,
That ate the malt
That lay in the house that Jack built.

This is the cat,
That killed the rat,
That ate the malt
That lay in the house that Jack built.

This is the dog,
That worried the cat,
That killed the rat,
That ate the malt
That lay in the house that Jack built.

This is the cow with the crumpled horn,
That tossed the dog,
That worried the cat,
That killed the rat,
That ate the malt
That lay in the house that Jack built.

This is the maiden all forlorn,
That milked the cow with the crumpled horn,
That tossed the dog,
That worried the cat,
That killed the rat,
That ate the malt
That lay in the house that Jack built.

This is the man all tattered and torn,
That kissed the maiden all forlorn,
That milked the cow with the crumpled horn,
That tossed the dog,
That worried the cat,
That killed the rat,
That ate the malt
That lay in the house that Jack built.

This is the priest all shaven and shorn,
That married the man all tattered and torn,
That kissed the maiden all forlorn,
That milked the cow with the crumpled horn,
That tossed the dog,
That worried the cat,
That killed the rat,
That ate the malt
That lay in the house that Jack built.

This is the cock that crowed in the morn,
That waked the priest all shaven and shorn,
That married the man all tattered and torn,
That kissed the maiden all forlorn,
That milked the cow with the crumpled horn,
That tossed the dog,
That worried the cat,
That killed the rat,
That ate the malt
That lay in the house that Jack built.

This is the farmer sowing his corn,
That kept the cock that crowed in the morn,
That waked the priest all shaven and shorn,
That married the man all tattered and torn,
That kissed the maiden all forlorn,
That milked the cow with the crumpled horn,
That tossed the dog,
That worried the cat,
That killed the rat,
That ate the malt
That lay in the house that Jack built.

Boys and Girls Come Out to Play

Boys and girls come out to play,
The moon doth shine as bright as day.
Leave your supper and leave your sleep,
And join your playfellows in the street.
Come with a whoop and come with a call,
Come with a good will or not at all.
Up the ladder and down the wall,
A half-penny loaf will serve us all;
You find milk, and I'll find flour,
and we'll have a pudding in half an hour.

Jack Be Nimble

Jack be nimble,
  Jack be quick,
Jack jump over
  The candlestick.

Ring-a-Ring O' Roses

Ring-a-ring o' roses,
A pocket full of posies,
  A-tishoo! A-tishoo!
We all fall down.

See-Saw, Margery Daw

See-saw, Margery Daw,
Jacky shall have a new master;
Jacky must have but a penny a day,
Because he can't work any faster.

Pease Porridge Hot

Pease porridge hot,
  Pease porridge cold,
Pease porridge in the pot
  Nine days old.

Some like it hot,
  Some like it cold,
Some like it in the pot
  Nine days old.

61

Early to Bed and Early to Rise

The cock crows in the morn
To tell us to rise,
And he that lies late
Will never be wise:
For early to bed,
And early to rise,
Is the way to be healthy
And wealthy and wise.

Star-Light, Star-Bright

Star-light, star-bright,
First star I see tonight;
I wish I may, I wish I might,
Have the wish I wish tonight.

Moon-Come-Out
by Eleanor Farjeon

Moon-Come-Out
And Sun-Go-In,
Here's a soft blanket
To cuddle your chin.

Moon-Go-In
And Sun-Come-Out
Throw off the blanket
And bustle about.

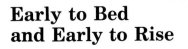

I See the Moon

I see the moon,
　And the moon sees me;
God bless the moon,
　And God bless me.

Good Night

by Rose Fyleman

The rabbits play no more,
  The little birds are weary,
The buttercups are folded up—
  Good night, good night, my dearie.

The children in the country,
  The children in the city,
Go to their beds with nodding heads—
  Good night, good night, my pretty.

Down with the Lambs

Down with the lambs,
  Up with the lark,
Run to bed, children,
  Before it gets dark.

Now I Lay Me Down to Sleep

Now I lay me down to sleep,
I pray the Lord my soul to keep;
And if I die before I wake,
I pray the Lord my soul to take.

A Bedtime Prayer

Matthew, Mark, Luke, and John,
Bless the bed that I lie on.
  Four corners to my bed,
  Four angels round my head;
  One to watch and one to pray
  And two to bear my soul away.

Folk & Fairy Tales

The Three Billy Goats Gruff

a Norwegian folk tale
by P. C. Asbjörnsen and J. Moe
adapted from the translation by G. W. Dasent

Once upon a time there were three Billy Goats who wanted to go up to the hillside to make themselves fat, and the name of all three was "Gruff."

On the way up, they had to cross a bridge over a stream. And under this bridge lived a great ugly Troll with eyes as big as saucers and a nose as long as a poker.

The first to cross the bridge was the youngest Billy Goat Gruff. *"Trip, trap! Trip, trap!"* went his hoofs on the bridge.

"Who's that trip-trapping over my bridge?" roared the Troll.

"Oh! It is only I, the tiniest Billy Goat Gruff. I am going up to the hillside to make myself fat," said the Billy Goat in a very small voice.

"Well, I'm coming to gobble you up!" said the Troll.

"Oh, no! Please do not take me. I'm too little, that I am," said the Billy Goat. "Wait a bit till the second Billy Goat Gruff comes. He's much bigger."

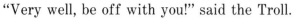

"Very well, be off with you!" said the Troll.

A little while later, the second Billy Goat Gruff came across the bridge. "Trip, trap! Trip, trap! Trip, trap!" went his hoofs on the bridge.

"Who's that trip-trapping over my bridge?" roared the Troll.

"Oh! It's the second Billy Goat Gruff. I am going up to make myself fat," said the Billy Goat in a strong voice.

"Well, I'm coming to gobble you up!" said the Troll.

"Oh, no! Don't take me. Wait a bit till the big Billy Goat Gruff comes. He's much bigger."

"Very well, be off with you!" said the Troll.

Just then, along came the big Billy Goat Gruff. **"Trip, trap! Trip, trap! Trip, trap! Trip, trap!"** went his hoofs on the bridge. The big Billy Goat Gruff was so heavy, the bridge creaked and groaned under him.

"Who's that trip-trapping over my bridge?" roared the Troll.

"It is I! The big Billy Goat Gruff!" said the Billy Goat, who had a very loud voice of his own.

"Well, I'm coming to gobble you up," roared the Troll. Then the big Billy Goat Gruff said:

> "Well, come along! I've got two spears,
> And I'll poke your eyeballs out at your ears;
> I've got besides two curling stones,
> And I'll crush you to bits, body and bones!"

That was what the big Billy Goat Gruff said. And so he rushed at the Troll and poked his eyes out with his horns, and crushed him to bits, body and bones. Then he tossed him into the stream. After that he went up to the hillside.

There, the three Billy Goats Gruff got so fat they were hardly able to walk home again. And if they haven't gotten thinner, why they're still fat; and so,

> Snip, snap, snout,
> This tale's told out.

The Gingerbread Boy

an American folk tale

There was once a little old man and a little old woman,
who lived in a little old house at the edge of a wood.
They would have been a very happy old couple but for
one thing—they had no little child, and they wished for
one very much.

One day, when the little old woman was baking
gingerbread, she cut a cake in the shape of a little boy
and put it into the oven. Presently, she went to the oven
to see if it was baked. As soon as the oven door was
opened, the little Gingerbread Boy jumped out and
began to run away as fast as he could go.

The little old woman called her husband, and they
both ran after him. But they could not catch him.

Soon, the Gingerbread Boy came to a barn where men
were threshing wheat. He called out to the men as he
went by, saying:

> "I've run away from a little old woman,
> A little old man,
> And I can run away from you, I can!"

Then all the men in the barn set out to run after him.
But, though they ran fast, they could not catch him.

The Gingerbread Boy ran on till he came to a field full of mowers. He called out to them:

"I've run away from a little old woman,
A little old man,
A barn full of threshers,
And I can run away from you, I can!"

Then the mowers began to run after him, but they couldn't catch him.

The Gingerbread Boy ran on till he came to a cow. He called out to her:

"I've run away from a little old woman,
A little old man,
A barn full of threshers,
A field full of mowers,
And I can run away from you, I can!"

Though the cow started at once, she couldn't catch him. Soon, the Gingerbread Boy came to a pig. He called out to the pig:

> "I've run away from a little old woman,
> A little old man,
> A barn full of threshers,
> A field full of mowers,
> A cow,
> And I can run away from you, I can!"

The pig ran after him, but couldn't catch him.

The Gingerbread Boy ran till he came across a fox, and to him he called out:

> "I've run away from a little old woman,
> A little old man,
> A barn full of threshers,
> A field full of mowers,
> A cow and a pig,
> And I can run away from you, I can!"

Then the fox set out after him. Now foxes can run very fast, and so the fox soon caught the Gingerbread Boy and began to eat him.

Presently the Gingerbread Boy said, "Oh, dear! I'm a quarter gone!" And then, "Oh, I'm half gone!" And soon, "I'm three-quarters gone!" And at last, "I'm all gone!" And that was the end of the Gingerbread Boy.

The Three Bears

an English folk tale

Once upon a time there were three Bears who lived in a
little house in the woods. There was a Great Big Father
Bear with a great big voice, and a Middle-Sized Mother
Bear with a middle-sized voice, and a Little Wee Baby
Bear with a little wee voice.

One morning the three Bears had porridge for
breakfast. The Mother Bear said, "This porridge is too
hot to eat. Let us go for a walk until it cools."

So the three Bears went for a walk in the woods.

While they were gone, along came a little girl named
Goldilocks. Seeing the little house, she wondered who
lived there, so she knocked at the door. No one
answered, so she knocked again. Still no one answered,
so Goldilocks opened the door and walked in.

There before her, in the little room, she saw a table
set for three. There was a great big bowl of porridge, a
middle-sized bowl of porridge, and a little wee bowl of
porridge. She tasted the great big bowl of porridge. "Oh,
this is too hot!" she said.

Then she tasted the middle-sized bowl of porridge.
"Oh, this is too cold!"

Then she tasted the little wee bowl of porridge. "Oh,
this is just right!" she said, and ate it all up.

She went into another room. There she saw three
chairs. There was a great big chair, a middle-sized chair,

and a little wee chair. Goldilocks sat down in the great
big chair. "Oh, this is too hard!" she said.

Then she sat down in the middle-sized chair. "Oh, this
is too soft!"

Then she sat in the little wee chair. "Oh, this is just
right!" But even as she said this, the chair broke.

Then she went into another room. There she saw three
beds. There was a great big bed, and a middle-sized bed,

and a little wee bed. Goldilocks lay down on the great big bed. "Oh, this is too hard!" she said.

Then she tried the middle-sized bed. "Oh, this is too soft!"

Then she tried the little wee bed. "Oh, this is just right!" she sighed. And pulling up the covers, she fell fast asleep.

By this time, the three Bears thought their porridge would be cool enough, so they returned from their walk in the woods.

When the Great Big Father Bear saw a spoon in his porridge bowl, he said in his great big voice:

"Someone has been eating my porridge!"

When the Middle-Sized Mother Bear saw a spoon in her porridge bowl, she said in her middle-sized voice:

"Someone has been eating my porridge!"

And the Little Wee Baby Bear, seeing a spoon in his porridge bowl, said in his little wee voice:

"Someone has been eating my porridge and has eaten it all up!"

Then the three Bears went into the next room. When the Great Big Father Bear saw that the cushion on his chair was out of place, he said in his great big voice:

"Someone has been sitting in my chair!"

When the Middle-Sized Mother Bear saw that the cushion on her chair was all pushed in, she said in her middle-sized voice:

"Someone has been sitting in my chair!"

And the Little Wee Baby Bear took one look at his chair and cried in his little wee voice:

"Someone has been sitting in my chair and broken the seat!"

Then the three Bears went into their bedroom. As soon as the Great Big Father Bear saw the wrinkled blankets on his bed, he said in his great big voice:

"Someone has been lying on my bed!"

When the Middle-Sized Mother Bear saw that the spread on her bed was pulled back, she said in her middle-sized voice:

"Someone has been lying on my bed!"

And when the Little Wee Baby Bear looked at his bed, he cried in his little wee voice:

"Someone has been lying on my bed—and there she is!"

Now Goldilocks was sleeping so soundly, the great big voice of the Great Big Father Bear was only like the roaring of the wind. And the middle-sized voice of the Middle-Sized Mother Bear was like someone speaking in a dream. But the little wee voice of the Little Wee Baby Bear was so sharp and shrill it woke her up at once.

When she saw the three Bears looking at her, she leaped from the bed, ran across the room, and jumped out of the low window. Then she ran through the woods as fast as ever her legs could carry her. Whatever happened to her, I do not know, but the three Bears never saw her again.

Why the Bear Has a Stumpy Tail

a Norwegian folk tale
by P. C. Asbjörnsen and J. Moe
adapted from the translation by G. W. Dasent

One winter day, the Bear met the Fox, who was slinking along with a string of fish he had stolen.

"Hi, stop a minute, Mr. Fox! Where did you get those fish?" demanded the Bear.

Now the Fox, as you know, is a sly one indeed. He didn't want the Bear to know that he had stolen the fish. So he said, "Oh, my Lord Bruin, I've been out fishing and caught them."

Well, the Bear was hungry and thought he would enjoy some fish. So he asked the Fox to tell him how to go about catching fish.

"Oh, it is quite easy," answered the fox, "and soon learned. You have only to go down to the river and cut a hole in the ice. Then you put your tail in the hole and keep it there as long as you can. Don't mind if it hurts a little. That will be the fish biting. The longer you keep your tail in the hole, the more fish you will catch. Then, all at once, pull out your tail. But be sure to give a good hard pull."

Well, the Bear did as the Fox said. Before long, he was very cold and his tail really hurt. But he kept his tail in the hole until he was sure that he must have caught a great many fish.

Then, remembering what the Fox had said, he gave a really hard pull. But what he didn't know was that his tail was frozen in the ice. So, when he pulled, his tail snapped off short. And that is why, to this day, the Bear has a stumpy tail.

The Little Red Hen

an English folk tale

One day the Little Red Hen was scratching in the farmyard, when she found a grain of wheat.

"Who will plant the wheat?" said she.

"Not I," said the duck.

"Not I," said the cat.

"Not I," said the dog.

"Very well then," said the Little Red Hen, "I will." So she planted the grain of wheat.

After some time the wheat grew tall and ripe.

"Who will cut the wheat?" asked the Little Red Hen.

"Not I," said the duck.

"Not I," said the cat.

"Not I," said the dog.

"Very well then, I will," said the Little Red Hen. So she cut the wheat.

"Now," she said, "who will thresh the wheat?"

"Not I," said the duck.

"Not I," said the cat.

"Not I," said the dog.

"Very well then, I will," said the Little Red Hen. So she threshed the wheat.

When the wheat was threshed, she said, "Who will take the wheat to the mill to have it ground into flour?"

"Not I," said the duck.

"Not I," said the cat.

"Not I," said the dog.

"Very well then, I will," said the Little Red Hen. So she took the wheat to the mill.

When the wheat was ground into flour, she said, "Who will make this flour into bread?"

"Not I," said the duck.

"Not I," said the cat.

"Not I," said the dog.

"Very well then, I will," said the Little Red Hen, and she baked a lovely loaf of bread.

Then she said, "Who will eat the bread?"

"Oh! I will," said the duck.

"Oh! I will," said the cat.

"Oh! I will," said the dog.

"Oh, no you won't!" said the Little Red Hen. "I will."

And she called her chicks and shared the bread with them.

The Cat on the Dovrefell

a Norwegian folk tale
by P. C. Asbjörnsen and J. Moe
adapted from the translation by G. W. Dasent

Once upon a time there was a man in Norway who
caught a great white bear. He decided that he would
give the bear to the King of Denmark. Now, it so fell
out that on his journey he came to that part of Norway
called the Dovrefell on Christmas Eve. Stopping at a
cottage where a man named Halvor lived, he asked if he
and his bear could stay the night.

"Heaven help me if what I say isn't true!" said
Halvor. "We can't let anyone stay tonight. Every
Christmas Eve such a pack of Trolls comes down upon
us that we are forced to flee. We haven't so much as a
roof over our own heads, to say nothing of lending one
to anyone else."

"Oh?" said the man. "If that's all it is, you can very
well lend me your house. My bear can lie under the stove
and I can sleep in the side room."

Well, the man begged so hard that, at last, he was
allowed to stay there. All the people of the house soon
left. But before they went, everything was got ready for
the Trolls. The tables were laid with rice porridge, boiled
fish, sausages, and all else that was good, just as for
any grand feast.

So, when everything was ready, down came the Trolls.
Some were great, and some were small. Some had long
tails, and some had no tails at all. And some had long,
long noses. They ate and drank everything.

Then, one of the little Trolls caught sight of the white
bear under the stove. He took a piece of sausage and
stuck it on a fork. Then he went and poked the sausage
up against the bear's nose, screaming, "Pussy, will you
have some sausage?"

The white bear rose up, gave a terrible growl, and
chased the whole pack of Trolls, both great and small,
out the door.

The next year, Halvor was out in the woods on the
afternoon of Christmas Eve. He was cutting wood
before the holidays, for he thought the Trolls would
come again. While he was hard at work, he heard a voice
in the woods calling out:

"Halvor! Halvor!"

"Well," said Halvor, "here I am."

"Have you got your big cat with you still?"

"Yes, that I have," said Halvor. "She's lying at home
under the stove. And what's more, she now has seven
kittens, far bigger and fiercer than she is herself."

"Oh, then, we'll never come to see you again," cried
out the Troll in the woods. And he kept his word. Ever
since that time, the Trolls have never eaten their
Christmas dinner with Halvor on the Dovrefell.

The Three Little Pigs

an English folk tale

Once upon a time there was a Mother Pig with three Little Pigs. As she did not have enough money to keep them, she sent them out to seek their fortune.

The first Little Pig met a Man with a bundle of straw and said to him, "Please, Man, give me that straw to build a house." The Man did, and the Little Pig built a house of straw.

Presently, a Wolf came along and knocked at the door. The Wolf said, "Little Pig, Little Pig, let me come in."

To which the Little Pig answered, "No, no, not by the hair on my chinny chin chin."

"Then I'll huff and I'll puff, and I'll blow your house in!" said the Wolf. So he huffed and he puffed, and he blew the house in, and ate up the Little Pig.

The second Little Pig met a Man with a bundle of

sticks and said, "Please, Man, give me those sticks to build a house." The Man did, and the Little Pig built a house of sticks.

Then along came the Wolf and said, "Little Pig, Little Pig, let me come in."

"No, no, not by the hair on my chinny chin chin," said the second Little Pig.

"Then I'll puff and I'll huff, and I'll blow your house in!" said the Wolf. So he huffed and he puffed, and he puffed and he huffed, and at last he blew the house down, and ate up the second Little Pig.

The third Little Pig met a Man with a load of bricks,

and said, "Please, Man, give me those bricks to build a house." The Man did, and the third Little Pig built a house of bricks.

Then the Wolf came along and said, as he had to the other Little Pigs, "Little Pig, Little Pig, let me come in."

"No, no, not by the hair on my chinny chin chin," said the third Little Pig.

"Then I'll huff and I'll puff, and I'll blow your house in," cried the Wolf. Well, he huffed and he puffed, and he puffed and he huffed, and he huffed and he puffed. But he could not blow the house down. When he found that he could not, with all his huffing and puffing, blow

the house down, he said, "Little Pig, I know where there
is a nice field of turnips."

"Where?" asked the Little Pig.

"Oh, in Mr. Smith's field. If you will be ready
tomorrow morning, I will call for you and we will go
together and get some for dinner."

"Very well," said the Little Pig, "I'll be ready. What
time do you mean to go?"

"At six o'clock," said the Wolf.

Well, the Little Pig got up at five, got the turnips,
and was home again before six. When the Wolf came he
said, "Little Pig, are you ready?"

"*Ready?*" asked the Little Pig. "I have been and come
back again. I have a nice potful of turnips for dinner."

The Wolf was very angry, but he still thought he could
trick the Little Pig somehow or other. So he said, "Little
Pig, I know where there is a nice apple tree."

"Where?" asked the Little Pig.

"Down at Merry-Garden," replied the Wolf. "If you promise not to fool me, I will come for you at five o'clock tomorrow and we will get some apples."

Well, the Little Pig woke at four the next morning and went off to get the apples. He hoped to be back before the Wolf came, but he had farther to go and also had to climb the tree. Just as he was coming down from the tree, he saw the Wolf coming. As you may suppose, that frightened him very much.

When the Wolf came up he said, "Little Pig, what are you doing here before me? Are they nice apples?"

"Yes, very," said the Little Pig; "I will throw you down one." And he threw it as far as he could. While the Wolf was gone to pick it up, the Little Pig jumped down and ran home.

The next day the Wolf came again, and said to the Little Pig, "Little Pig, there is a Fair in the town this afternoon. Will you go?"

"Oh, yes," said the Little Pig, "I'll go. What time will you be ready?"

"At three," said the Wolf.

So the Little Pig went off early, as usual, got to the Fair, bought a butter churn, and was on his way home with it when he saw the Wolf coming. At first he did not know what to do. He got into the butter churn to hide. In doing so, he turned it round so that it began to roll. And it rolled down the hill with the Little Pig inside it. The Wolf was so frightened by this that he ran home without going to the Fair.

Later, the Wolf went to the Little Pig's house and told him how frightened he had been by a great round thing which came down the hill past him.

Then the Little Pig said, "Hah! I frightened you, did I? I had been to the Fair and bought a butter churn. When I saw you, I got into it and rolled down the hill."

Then the Wolf was very angry indeed. He declared he *would* eat up the Little Pig, and that he would climb down the chimney after him.

When the Little Pig saw what the Wolf was about, he put a pot full of water in the fireplace and made a blazing fire. Just as the Wolf was coming down the chimney, the Little Pig took the cover off the pot and in fell the Wolf! The Little Pig put the cover on again, instantly boiled up the Wolf, ate him for supper, and lived happily ever after.

The Shoemaker and the Elves

adapted from a German fairy tale
by the Brothers Grimm

There was once a shoemaker who worked very hard but was also very poor. At last, all he had was just enough leather to make one pair of shoes. He cut out the shoes in the evening so that he could set to work on them the next morning. Then he went to bed and, leaving all his cares to heaven, fell asleep.

In the morning, when he went down to work, he found the pair of shoes made and finished, and standing on his table. He was very much astonished, and did not know what to think.

After a moment, the poor man took the shoes in his hand to look at them more closely. They were beautifully made. Every stitch was in its right place, just as if they had come from the hand of a master workman.

Soon after, a buyer came in. The shoes fitted him very well, so he gave more than the usual price for them. Now the shoemaker had enough money to buy leather for two pairs of shoes. He cut out the shoes that night, intending to set to work the next morning.

But that was not to be. When he got up in the
morning, the two pairs of shoes were already finished. A
customer paid him so much money for these shoes that
he was able to buy leather enough for four new pairs.

Early next morning he found the four pairs finished.
And so it always happened. Whatever he cut out in the
evening was worked up by the morning. He was soon
making a good living, and in the end became very
well-to-do.

One night, not long before Christmas, when the
shoemaker had finished cutting out shoes, and before he
went to bed, he said to his wife, "How would it be if we
were to sit up tonight and see who it is that makes the
shoes?"

His wife agreed, and left a light burning. They both hid behind a curtain in a corner of the room and watched to see what would happen.

As soon as it was midnight, two naked little elves came in and seated themselves at the shoemaker's table. They began to stitch, to pierce, and to hammer so cleverly and quickly with their little fingers that the shoemaker's eyes could scarcely follow them. They did not stop until everything was finished and ready on the table. Then they jumped up and disappeared as quickly as they had come.

The next morning, the shoemaker's wife said to her husband, "Those little men have made us rich. We ought to show our thanks. With all their running about, and having nothing to cover them, they must be very cold. I'll tell you what: I will make little shirts, coats, waistcoats, and breeches for them, and knit each of them a pair of stockings. And you shall make each of them a little pair of shoes."

The thought pleased the good man very much. One night, when everything was finished, instead of the cut-out work, they laid the gifts on the table. Then they hid themselves so that they could see what the elves would do.

When midnight came, the elves rushed in, ready to set to work. But when they found the neat little garments instead of cut-out leather, they stood a moment in surprise. Then they showed the greatest delight. Swiftly, they took up the clothes and slipped them on, singing,

> *What spruce and dandy boys are we!*
> *No longer cobblers we will be.*

Then they hopped and skipped and leaped over chairs and benches. At last they danced out the door and into the night.

The shoemaker never saw them again. But from that time on, everything went well with the shoemaker as long as he lived.

Lazy Jack

an English folk tale

Once upon a time there was a boy named Jack. He lived with his mother in a small house in a small village. Jack and his mother were very poor. What little money they had, the old woman earned by spinning wool into thread.

But Jack did nothing, for he was very lazy. In summer, he sat all day in the shade of a huge tree. In winter, he sat all day by the fire. His mother could not get him to do anything to help her. Finally, the old woman had had enough.

"You lazy boy!" she shouted. "If you do not go to work for your porridge, I will turn you out of the house."

Frightened by his mother's threat, Jack thought he had best go to work if he wanted to eat. The very next day he went out and hired himself to a neighboring farmer for a penny. After he got his penny, Jack was very pleased. He had never had any money before. As he walked home, he kept tossing the penny into the air and catching it. But as he crossed a bridge, Jack dropped his penny. He watched in dismay as it rolled off the bridge and into the river below.

When his mother learned what had happened she was very angry. "You stupid boy," she said. "You should put the penny in your pocket."

"I'll do so the next time," said Jack.

The next day Jack went out and hired himself to a cowherd. This man gave Jack a jar of milk for his day's work. Remembering what his mother had said, Jack put the jar of milk into the large pocket of his jacket. Long before he got home, all the milk had spilled out.

"Dear me, you foolish boy," his mother said. "You should have carried the jar of milk on your head."

"I'll do so the next time," replied Jack.

The next day Jack again hired himself to a farmer.
The farmer agreed to give Jack a cream cheese for his
work. In the evening, Jack took the cheese. Remembering
what his mother had said, Jack put the cheese on his
head and started home. But by the time he got home
most of the cheese had melted and run into his hair.

"You stupid lout!" his mother shouted. "You should
have carried the cheese very carefully in your hands."

"I'll do so the next time," replied Jack.

The following day Jack went out and hired himself to
a baker. When Jack had finished work, the baker gave
him a large tomcat. Remembering what his mother had
said, Jack carried the cat very carefully in his hands.
But in a short time the cat had scratched him so much
he had to let it go.

When he got home, his mother said to him, "You silly
boy. You should have tied a string to the cat and
dragged it along after you."

"I'll do so the next time," replied Jack.

The next day Jack hired himself to a butcher. This good

man paid Jack with a leg of lamb. Remembering what his mother had said, Jack tied a string to the leg of lamb and dragged it through the dirt after him. By the time Jack reached home, the meat was spoiled.

This time, Jack's mother was out of patience with him. The next day was Sunday, and now they would

have nothing but boiled cabbage for their Sunday dinner.

"You ninny-hammer!" she cried. "You should have carried the leg of lamb on your shoulder."

"I'll do so the next time," replied Jack.

Well, on Monday, Lazy Jack went out once more to look for work. This time he hired himself to a cattlekeeper. At the end of the day, the man gave Jack a donkey. Remembering what his mother had said, Jack hoisted the donkey onto his shoulders. Although he was very strong, Jack had difficulty doing this. At last, however, he got the donkey up on his shoulders and started home.

Now it happened that on his way home Jack had to pass the house of a very rich man. This man had an only daughter, who was very beautiful. Unfortunately, she could not speak or hear, and she had never laughed in her life. The doctors had told her father that she would never speak or hear until someone made her laugh. Many people tried, but without success. At last, despairing of all hope, her father offered to give her in marriage to the first man who could make her laugh.

Now it happened that the young lady was looking out the window as Jack struggled along with the donkey on his shoulders. The poor beast, its legs sticking up in the air, was kicking violently and hee-hawing with all its might. Well, the sight was so funny the young lady burst into laughter. Instantly she recovered her speech and her hearing.

Her father was overjoyed. He kept his promise, and gave her to Jack in marriage. He also made Jack a rich man.

After Jack and the girl were married, they went to live in a large house. And Jack's mother lived with them in great happiness for the rest of her life.

The Five Chinese Brothers

a Chinese folk tale
retold by Claire Huchet Bishop

Once upon a time there were Five Chinese Brothers and they all looked exactly alike. They lived with their mother in a little house not far from the sea.

The First Chinese Brother could swallow the sea.
The Second Chinese Brother had an iron neck.
The Third Chinese Brother could stretch and stretch and stretch his legs.
The Fourth Chinese Brother could not be burned.
The Fifth Chinese Brother could hold his breath indefinitely.

Every morning the First Chinese Brother would go fishing, and whatever the weather, he would come back to the village with beautiful and rare fish which he had caught and could sell at the market for a very good price.

One day, as he was leaving the market place, a little boy stopped him and asked him if he could go fishing with him.

"No, it could not be done," said the First Chinese
Brother.

But the little boy begged and begged and finally the
First Chinese Brother consented. "Under one condition,"
said he, "and that is that you shall obey me promptly."

"Yes, yes," the little boy promised.

Early next morning, the First Chinese Brother and
the little boy went down to the beach.

"Remember," said the First Chinese Brother, "you
must obey me promptly. When I make a sign for you to
come back, you must come at once."

"Yes, yes," the little boy promised.

Then the First Chinese Brother swallowed the sea.

And all the fish were left high and dry at the bottom
of the sea. And all the treasures of the sea lay
uncovered.

The little boy was delighted. He ran here and there

stuffing his pockets with strange pebbles, extraordinary shells, and fantastic algae.

Near the shore the First Chinese Brother gathered some fish while he kept holding the sea in his mouth. Presently he grew tired. It is very hard to hold the sea. So he made a sign with his hand for the little boy to come back. The little boy saw him but paid no attention.

The First Chinese Brother made great movements with his arms and that meant "Come back!" But did the little boy care? Not a bit and he ran further away.

Then the First Chinese Brother felt the sea swelling inside him and he made desperate gestures to call the little boy back. But the little boy made faces at him and fled as fast as he could.

The First Chinese Brother held the sea until he thought he was going to burst. All of a sudden the sea forced its way out of his mouth, went back to its bed . . . and the little boy disappeared.

When the First Chinese Brother returned to the village, alone, he was arrested, put in prison, tried and condemned to have his head cut off.

On the morning of the execution he said to the judge:

"Your Honor, will you allow me to go and bid my mother good-bye?"

"It is only fair," said the judge.

So the First Chinese Brother went home ... and the Second Chinese Brother came back in his place.

All the people were assembled on the village square to witness the execution. The executioner took his sword and struck a mighty blow.

But the Second Chinese Brother got up and smiled. He was the one with the iron neck and they simply could not cut his head off. Everybody was angry and they decided that he should be drowned.

On the morning of the execution, the Second Chinese Brother said to the judge:

"Your Honor, will you allow me to go and bid my mother good-bye?"

"It is only fair," said the judge.

So the Second Chinese Brother went home ... and the Third Chinese Brother came back in his place.

He was pushed on a boat which made for the open sea.

When they were far out on the ocean, the Third Chinese Brother was thrown overboard.

But he began to S-T-R-E-T-C-H and S-T-R-E-T-C-H and S—T—R—E—T—C—H his legs, way down to the bottom of the sea, and all the time his smiling face was bobbing up and down on the crest of the waves. He simply could not be drowned.

Everybody was very angry, and they all decided that he should be burned.

On the morning of the execution, the Third Chinese Brother said to the judge:

"Your Honor, will you allow me to go and bid my mother good-bye?"

"It is only fair," said the judge.

So the Third Chinese Brother went home ... and the Fourth Chinese Brother came back in his place.

He was tied up to a stake. Fire was set to it and all

the people stood around watching it. In the midst of the flames they heard him say:

"This is quite pleasant."

"Bring some more wood!" the people cried.

The fire roared higher.

"Now it is quite comfortable," said the Fourth Chinese Brother, for he was the one who could not be burned. Everybody was getting more and more angry every minute and they all decided to smother him.

On the morning of the execution, the Fourth Chinese Brother said to the judge:

"Your Honor, will you allow me to go and bid my mother good-bye?"

"It is only fair," said the judge.

So the Fourth Chinese Brother went home ... and the Fifth Chinese Brother came back in his place. A large brick oven had been built on the village square and it had been all stuffed with whipped cream. The Fifth Chinese Brother was shovelled into the oven, right in the middle of the cream, the door was shut tight, and everybody sat around and waited.

They were not going to be tricked again! So they

stayed there all night and even a little after dawn, just to make sure.

Then they opened the door and pulled him out. And he shook himself and said, "My! That was a good sleep!"

Everybody stared open-mouthed and round-eyed. But the judge stepped forward and said, "We have tried to get rid of you in every possible way and somehow it cannot be done. It must be that you are innocent."

"Yes, yes," shouted all the people. So they let him go and he went home.

And the Five Chinese Brothers and their mother all lived together happily for many years.

Cinderella

adapted from a French fairy tale
by Charles Perrault

Once upon a time, there was a gentleman who married
for his second wife the proudest and most disagreeable
woman that was ever seen. She had two daughters who
were exactly like her in all ways. He himself had a
young daughter, but she was very sweet and good.

No sooner was the wedding over but the stepmother
began to show how mean she really was. She could not
bear the good qualities of this pretty girl, who was so
unlike her own daughters. So she gave her the hardest
and dirtiest work: washing the dishes and tables,
dusting the rooms, and cleaning the fireplace. And she
had to sleep in a tiny attic room, on an old wretched
straw bed.

The poor girl suffered in silence, not daring to tell her
father, for he was ruled by his new wife. When she had
done her work, she used to go into the chimney corner
and sit down among cinders and ashes. Because of this,
her stepsisters gave her the nickname "Cinderella."
However, in spite of her shabby clothes, Cinderella was
a hundred times more beautiful than her stepsisters,
though they always dressed very richly.

It happened that the king's son gave a ball to which all the important people, including the two sisters, were invited. They were delighted, and busied themselves deciding what to wear. This was a new trouble to Cinderella, for it was she who ironed her sisters' linen and plaited their ruffles, while they talked all day long of nothing but their clothes.

"For my part," said the elder, "I will wear my red-velvet suit with trimmings of French lace."

"And I," said the younger, "shall have my usual petticoat. But I will put on my gold-flowered gown and my diamond necklace which is far finer than anything you have."

Cinderella was often called upon for advice, and on the evening of the ball offered to dress them herself and to do their hair. As she was doing this, the elder one said to her, "Cinderella, don't you wish you were going to the ball?"

"Alas," she said, "you are only making fun of me. It is not for such as I to go to the ball."

"You are right," said the younger one. "It would certainly make people laugh to see a cinderwench at a palace ball."

After this, anyone but Cinderella would have dressed them awry, but she was very good and did the job perfectly.

When they left for the palace, Cinderella followed the coach with her eyes as long as she could. After it had disappeared, she sat down by the kitchen fire and began to cry.

Instantly, her fairy godmother appeared beside her and asked, "Why all the tears, my child?"

"I wish I could—I wish I could—" She was not able to speak because of her tears and sobbing.

"You wish to go to the ball. Is it not so?"

"Yes," cried Cinderella, with a great sigh.

"Well," said her fairy godmother, "be a good girl, and I shall arrange for you to go." Then she said to her, "Run into the garden and bring me a pumpkin."

Cinderella went immediately to gather the finest pumpkin and brought it to her fairy godmother. But try as she might, she could not imagine how this pumpkin could help her get to the ball. Her fairy godmother took the pumpkin and scooped out all the inside. This done, she struck it with her wand, and the pumpkin was instantly turned into a fine coach, gilded all over with gold.

"Now bring me the mousetrap, child."

Cinderella immediately brought the trap, which contained six mice, all alive. She told Cinderella to lift up the little trap door. As each mouse went out, she gave it a little tap with her wand and changed it into a beautiful white horse.

Being at a loss for a coachman, Cinderella said, "I will go and see if there is a rat in the rat-trap—we may make a coachman of him."

"You are right," replied her fairy godmother. "Go and look."

Cinderella brought the trap to her, and in it there was a huge rat. The instant the fairy godmother touched him with her wand, he was turned into a fat, jolly coachman, who had the smartest whiskers eyes ever beheld. After that, she said to Cinderella, "Go again into the garden, and you will find six lizards behind the watering pot. Bring them to me."

Cinderella had no sooner done so than her fairy

godmother turned them into six footmen. They jumped up behind the coach as if they had done nothing else in their life. The fairy godmother then said to Cinderella, "Well, you see here everything you need to take you to the ball. Are you not pleased with it?"

"Oh, yes," cried Cinderella, "but must I go in these old rags?"

Her fairy godmother laughed and just touched her with her wand. In that instant, her old rags were turned into cloth of gold and silver, all sparkling with jewels. And on her feet she had a pair of glass slippers, the prettiest in the whole world.

As Cinderella climbed into the coach, her fairy godmother said to her, "Enjoy yourself at the ball, but remember, you must be home by midnight. If you stay one moment longer, the coach will become a pumpkin again. Your horses mice, your coachman a rat, your footmen lizards, and your clothes will turn to rags, just as they were before."

Cinderella promised she would leave the ball before midnight. And then away she drove, scarce able to contain herself for joy.

The king's son, who was told that a great princess, whom nobody knew, had come, ran out to meet her. He gave her his hand as she stepped down from the coach and led her into the hall. There was immediate silence. The people stopped dancing, and the violins ceased to play. Everyone whispered, "How beautiful she is!"

The king himself could not help watching her and telling the queen softly that it was a long time since he had seen so beautiful and lovely a creature. All the ladies studied her clothes carefully, planning to have some made the next day that would be just like them.

The king's son took her to a seat of honor, and then led her out to dance. She danced so gracefully that everyone admired her more and more. Later, at supper, the young prince ate nothing, he was so busy watching Cinderella.

As for Cinderella, she sat down by her sisters and showed them every courtesy. This surprised them very much, for they did not recognize her. Time passed very quickly, and Cinderella quite forgot what her godmother had commanded her.

Suddenly she heard a clock begin to strike, and realized that in a moment it would be midnight. She

then rose up and fled, as nimble as a deer. The prince followed but could not overtake her. She left behind one of her glass slippers which the prince took up most carefully. Cinderella reached home, quite out of breath, and in her old clothes, having nothing left of all her finery but one of the little slippers, the mate to the one she had dropped.

The prince asked the guards at the palace gate if they had seen a princess go out. They had seen nobody but a young girl, very poorly dressed.

When the two sisters returned from the ball, they were full of all that had happened. They told of this beautiful girl who had appeared, and then fled as the clock began to strike midnight. And, of course, they spoke of the glass slipper she had dropped in her haste. They said that the king's son had picked it up. He had done nothing but look at it the rest of the evening. Most certainly he was in love with the beautiful girl who owned the glass slipper.

What they said was very true. A few days afterward, the king's son caused it to be proclaimed, with sounds of trumpets, that he would marry the girl whose foot this slipper fit.

The next day, one of the heralds from the court began going from house to house with the glass slipper. One fine woman after another tried it on, but to no avail. It was a fairy slipper and no one could get a foot into it.

Finally, the slipper was brought to the two stepsisters. Each did all she possibly could to get her foot into the slipper. But they could not. Cinderella, who saw all this, and knew her slipper, said to them, laughing:

"Let me see if it will fit me."

Her stepsisters burst out laughing. But the gentleman who was sent to try the slipper said it was only right she should try. He had orders to let everyone try on the slipper.

He asked Cinderella to sit down. Putting the slipper to her foot, he found it went on easily and fitted her as if it had been made of wax.

The two stepsisters were astonished. But they were
even more astonished when Cinderella pulled out of her
pocket the other slipper and put it on her foot. At that
moment, in came her fairy godmother who touched
Cinderella's clothes with her wand and made them richer
and more magnificent than any she had worn before.

And now her two stepsisters knew her to be that fine,
beautiful lady they had seen at the ball. They threw
themselves at her feet and begged her pardon for all
they had said and done to her. Cinderella raised them up
and embraced them, saying that she forgave them with
all her heart and wished them to love her always.

Cinderella was taken immediately to the young prince.
He thought her more charming than ever and, a few
days after, married her. Cinderella, who was no less
good than beautiful, gave her two stepsisters a place to
live in the palace and before long saw them married to
great lords of the court.

Why Mosquitoes
Buzz in People's Ears

a West African folk tale
retold by Verna Aardema

One morning a mosquito saw an iguana drinking at a
waterhole. The mosquito said, "Iguana, you will never
believe what I saw yesterday."

"Try me," said the iguana.

The mosquito said, "I saw a farmer digging yams that
were almost as big as I am."

"What's a mosquito compared to a yam?" snapped the
iguana grumpily. "I would rather be deaf than listen to
such nonsense!" Then he stuck two sticks in his ears and
went off, *mek, mek, mek, mek,* through the reeds.

The iguana was still grumbling to himself when he
happened to pass by a python.

The big snake raised his head and said, "Good
morning, Iguana."

The iguana did not answer but lumbered on, bobbing
his head, *badamin, badamin.*

"Now, why won't he speak to me?" said the python to
himself. "Iguana must be angry about something. I'm
afraid he is plotting some mischief against me!" He
began looking for somewhere to hide. The first likely
place he found was a rabbit hole, and in it he went,
wasawusu, wasawusu, wasawusu.

When the rabbit saw the big snake coming into her burrow, she was terrified. She scurried out through her back way and bounded, *krik, krik, krik,* across a clearing.

A crow saw the rabbit running for her life. He flew into the forest crying *kaa, kaa, kaa!* It was his duty to spread the alarm in case of danger.

A monkey heard the crow. He was sure that some dangerous beast was prowling near. He began screeching and leaping *kili wili* through the trees to help warn the other animals.

As the monkey was crashing through the treetops, he happened to land on a dead limb. It broke and fell on an owl's nest, killing one of the owlets.

Mother Owl was not at home. For though she usually hunted only in the night, this morning she was still out searching for one more tidbit to satisfy her hungry babies. When she returned to the nest, she found one of them dead. Her other children told her that the monkey had killed it. All that day and all that night, she sat in her tree—so sad, so sad, so sad!

Now it was Mother Owl who woke the sun each day so that the dawn could come. But this time, when she should have hooted for the sun, she did not do it.

The night grew longer and longer. The animals of the forest knew it was lasting much too long. They feared that the sun would never come back.

At last King Lion called a meeting of the animals. They came and sat down, *pem, pem, pem,* around a council fire. Mother Owl did not come, so the antelope was sent to fetch her.

When she arrived, King Lion asked, "Mother Owl, why have you not called the sun? The night has lasted long, long, long, and everyone is worried."

Mother Owl said, "Monkey killed one of my owlets. Because of that, I cannot bear to wake the sun."

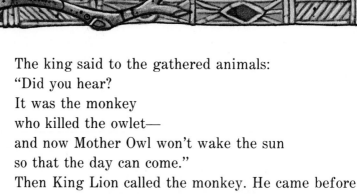

The king said to the gathered animals:
"Did you hear?
It was the monkey
who killed the owlet—
and now Mother Owl won't wake the sun
so that the day can come."

Then King Lion called the monkey. He came before him nervously glancing from side to side, *rim, rim, rim, rim.*

"Monkey," said the king, "why did you kill one of Mother Owl's babies?"

"Oh, King," said the monkey, "it was the crow's fault. He was calling and calling to warn us of danger. And I went leaping through the trees to help. A limb broke under me, and it fell *taaa* on the owl's nest."

The king said to the council:
"So, it was the crow
who alarmed the monkey,
who killed the owlet—
and now Mother Owl won't wake the sun
so that the day can come."
Then the king called for the crow. That big bird came
flapping up. He said, "King Lion, it was the rabbit's
fault! I saw her running for her life in the daytime.
Wasn't that reason enough to spread an alarm?"

The king nodded his head and said to the council:
"So, it was the rabbit
who startled the crow,
who alarmed the monkey,
who killed the owlet—
and now Mother Owl won't wake the sun
so that the day can come."

Then King Lion called the rabbit. The timid little creature stood before him, one trembling paw drawn up uncertainly.

"Rabbit," cried the king, "why did you break a law of nature and go running, running, running, in the daytime?"

"Oh, King," said the rabbit, "it was the python's fault. I was in my house minding my own business when that big snake came in and chased me out."

The king said to the council:
"So, it was the python
who scared the rabbit,
who startled the crow,
who alarmed the monkey,
who killed the owlet—
and now Mother Owl won't wake the sun
so that the day can come."

King Lion called the python, who came slithering, *wasawusu, wasawusu,* past the other animals.

"But, King," he cried, "it was the iguana's fault! He wouldn't speak to me. And I thought he was plotting some mischief against me. When I crawled into the rabbit's hole, I was only trying to hide."

The king said to the council:
"So, it was the iguana
who frightened the python,
who scared the rabbit,
who startled the crow,
who alarmed the monkey,
who killed the owlet—
and now Mother Owl won't wake the sun
so that the day can come."

Now the iguana was not at the meeting, for he had
not heard the summons.

The antelope was sent to fetch him.

All the animals laughed when they saw the iguana
coming, *badamin, badamin,* with the sticks still stuck in
his ears!

King Lion pulled out the sticks, *purup, purup.* Then
he asked, "Iguana, what evil have you been plotting
against the python?"

"None! None at all!" cried the iguana. "Python is my
friend!"

"Then why wouldn't you say good morning to me?"
demanded the snake.

"I didn't hear you, or even see you!" said the iguana.
"Mosquito told me such a big lie, I couldn't bear to listen
to it. So I put sticks in my ears."

"*Nge, nge, nge,*" laughed the lion. "So that's why you
had sticks in your ears!"

"Yes," said the iguana. "It was the mosquito's fault."
King Lion said to the council:
"So, it was the mosquito
who annoyed the iguana,
who frightened the python,
who scared the rabbit,
who startled the crow,
who alarmed the monkey,
who killed the owlet—
and now Mother Owl won't wake the sun
so that the day can come."

"Punish the mosquito! Punish the mosquito!" cried all the animals.

When Mother Owl heard that, she was satisfied. She turned her head toward the east and hooted: "Hoo! Hooooo! Hooooooo!"

And the sun came up.

Meanwhile the mosquito had listened to it all from a nearby bush. She crept under a curly leaf, *semm*, and was never found and brought before the council.

But because of this the mosquito has a guilty conscience. To this day she goes about whining in people's ears: *"Zeee!* Is everyone still angry at me?"

When she does that, she gets an honest answer. KPAO!

Jack and the Beanstalk

an English fairy tale

Once upon a time there was a poor widow who had an
only son named Jack and a cow named Milky-White.
And all they had to live on was the milk the cow gave
every morning, which they carried to the market and
sold. But one morning Milky-White gave no milk, and
they didn't know what to do.

"What shall we do, what shall we do?" cried the
widow, wringing her hands.

"Cheer up, mother, I'll go and get work somewhere,"
said Jack.

"We've tried that before, and nobody would take you,"
said his mother. "We must sell Milky-White and with
the money start a shop or something."

"All right, mother," said Jack. "It's market day today.
I'll soon sell Milky-White, and then we'll see what we
can do."

So he took the cow's halter in his hand and off he
started. He hadn't gone far when he met a funny-
looking old man who said to him, "Good morning, Jack."

"Good morning to you," said Jack, wondering how the
man knew his name.

"Well, Jack, where are you off to?" asked the man.

"I'm going to the market to sell our cow."

"Oh, you look the proper sort of chap to sell cows," said the man. "I wonder if you know how many beans make five?"

"Two in each hand and one in your mouth," said Jack, as sharp as a needle.

"Right you are," said the man. "And here they are, the very beans themselves," he went on, pulling out of his pocket a number of strange-looking beans. "As you are so sharp," said he, "I don't mind doing a swop with you—your cow for these beans."

"Go along," says Jack; "wouldn't you like that!"

"Ah! you don't know what these beans are," said the man. "If you plant them tonight, by morning they will grow right up to the sky."

"Really?" said Jack. "You don't say so."

"Yes, that is so. And if it doesn't turn out to be true, you can have your cow back."

"Right," said Jack, handing him Milky-White's halter and pocketing the beans.

As Jack hadn't gone very far, it wasn't even dusk by the time he got to his door.

"Back already, Jack?" said his mother. "I see you haven't got Milky-White, so you've sold her. How much did you get for her?"

"You'll never guess, mother," said Jack.

"What was it? Five pounds, ten, fifteen? No, it can't be twenty."

"I knew you couldn't guess. What do you say to these beans? They're magical, plant them tonight and—"

"What!" cried Jack's mother, "Have you been such a fool, such an idiot, as to give away my Milky-White for these beans? Take that! Take that! Take that! And as for your precious beans, here they go out the window! Now off with you to bed. There'll be no supper for you!"

So Jack went upstairs to his little room in the attic, a sad and sorry boy.

When Jack woke up, the room looked very strange.

The sun was shining into part of it, yet all the rest was
quite dark and shady. So Jack jumped up and dressed
himself and went to the window. And what do you think
he saw? Why, the beans his mother had thrown out of
the window into the garden had sprung up into a big
beanstalk that went up and up and up till it reached the
sky! So the man spoke truth after all.

The beanstalk grew quite close to Jack's window. All
he had to do was open the window and jump on to the
beanstalk, which ran up just like a big ladder.

Jack climbed and climbed and climbed till at last he
reached the sky. And when he got there he found a long,
broad road going as straight as an arrow. So he walked
along the road till he came to a great big tall house. And
on the doorstep there was a great big tall woman.

"Good morning, mum," said Jack, politely. "Could you
be so kind as to give me some breakfast?"

"It's breakfast you want, is it?" cried the great big
tall woman. "It's breakfast you'll be if you don't move
off from here. My man is an Ogre, and there's nothing
he likes better than boys broiled on toast."

"Oh! please mum, do give me something to eat. I've

had nothing to eat since yesterday morning, really and truly, mum."

Well, the Ogre's wife was not half as bad as she looked or sounded. So she took Jack into the kitchen and gave him some bread and cheese and a jug of milk. But Jack hadn't half finished when he heard a great **thump! thump! thump!** and the whole house began to tremble.

"Goodness gracious me! It's my old man," said the Ogre's wife. "What on earth shall I do? Come along quick and jump in here." And she bundled Jack into the oven just as the Ogre came in.

He was a big one, to be sure. At his belt he had three calves strung up by the heels. He unhooked them and threw them down on the table and said: "Here, wife, fix me these for breakfast. Ah, what's this I smell?

> *Fee-fi-fo-fum,*
> *I smell the blood of an Englishman.*
> *Be he alive, or be he dead,*
> *I'll have his bones to grind my bread."*

"Nonsense, dear," said his wife, "you're dreaming. Or perhaps you smell the scraps of that little boy you had for yesterday's dinner. Go and wash, and by the time you come back your breakfast'll be ready for you."

So off the Ogre went. Jack was just going to jump out of the oven and run away when the woman told him to stay. "Wait till he's asleep," she said. "He always has a nap after breakfast."

After breakfast, the Ogre went to a big chest and took out a couple of bags of gold. He sat down and began to count, till at last his head started to nod and he began to snore till the whole house shook.

Then Jack crept out of the oven. Taking one of the bags of gold, he ran until he came to the beanstalk. Then he threw down the bag of gold into his mother's garden and climbed down and down till at last he got home. He showed his mother the gold and said, "Well, mother, wasn't I right about the beans? They are really magical, you see."

They lived on the gold for some time, but at last it came to an end. So Jack made up his mind to try his luck once more up at the top of the beanstalk.

One fine morning he rose early and climbed and climbed and climbed till at last he came out to the road again and walked up it to the great big tall house. There, sure enough, was the great big tall woman standing on the doorstep.

"Good morning, mum," said Jack, as bold as brass. "Could you be so good as to give me something to eat?"

"Go away, my boy," said the big tall woman, "or else my man will eat you for breakfast. But aren't you the lad who came here once before? Do you know that very day my man missed one of his bags of gold?"

"That's strange, mum," said Jack, "I dare say I could tell you something about that, but I'm so hungry I can't speak till I've had something to eat."

Well, the big tall woman was so curious that she took Jack in and gave him something to eat. But he had scarcely begun munching it as slowly as he could when **thump! thump! thump!** they heard the giant's footsteps. "Into the oven with you!" cried the Ogre's wife. "You can tell me about the gold when he goes to sleep." In

came the Ogre, with three great oxen tied to his belt.
Throwing them down, he began to sniff the air.

> "Fee-fi-fo-fum,
> I smell the blood of an Englishman.
> Be he alive, or be he dead,
> I'll have his bones to grind my bread."

"Nonsense, dear," said his wife. "It's only the bones of
the boy you ate last week. They are still in the
garbage."

"Humph! Well, broil these oxen over the fire and I'll
have breakfast." After he had eaten, the Ogre said,
"Wife, bring me the hen that lays the golden eggs." So
she brought the hen and the Ogre said: "Lay," and it
laid an egg all of gold. And then the Ogre began to nod
his head and snore till the house shook.

Then Jack crept out of the oven, caught hold of the
golden hen, and was off before you could say "Jack
Robinson." But the hen gave a cackle which woke the
Ogre. Just as Jack got out of the house, he heard him
calling: "Wife, what have you done with my golden
hen?"

But that was all Jack heard, for he rushed to the
beanstalk and climbed down like a house on fire. When
he got home, he showed his mother the wonderful hen,
and said "Lay." And it laid a golden egg every time he
said "Lay."

Well, it wasn't long before Jack determined to have another try at his luck. So one fine morning, he rose early, got on to the beanstalk, and climbed and climbed and climbed till he got to the top. But this time he knew better than to go straight to the Ogre's house. When he got near it, he waited behind a bush till he saw the Ogre's wife come out with a pail to get some water. Jack then crept into the house and hid in a huge copper pot. He hadn't been there long when he heard **thump! thump! thump!** as before, and in came the Ogre and his wife.

"Fee-fi-fo-fum, I smell the blood of an Englishman," cried the Ogre. "I smell him, wife, I smell him."

"Do you, dearie?" said the Ogre's wife. "If it's that little rascal who stole your gold and the hen that laid the golden eggs, he's sure to be in the oven." And they both rushed to the oven. But Jack wasn't there, luckily, and the Ogre's wife said, "There you go again with your 'fee-fi-fo-fum.' Why of course it's the boy you caught last night that I've just broiled for your breakfast."

So the Ogre sat down to breakfast, but every now and then he would mutter, "Well, I could have sworn—" and he'd get up and search the cupboards. Luckily, he didn't think of the copper pot.

After breakfast was over, the Ogre called out, "Wife, wife, bring me my golden harp." So she brought out the little harp and put it on the table before him. Then he said: "Sing!" and the tiny golden harp sang most beautifully. And it went on singing till the Ogre fell asleep, and commenced to snore like thunder.

Then Jack very quietly lifted up the lid of the big pot, and got out like a mouse, and crept on hands and knees till he came to the table. He crawled up until he could reach the golden harp. Then he dropped to the floor and, holding the harp under his arm, dashed towards the door. But the harp called out, "Master! Master!" and the Ogre woke up just in time to see Jack running off with his harp.

Jack ran as fast as he could, and the Ogre came

rushing after him. When Jack got to the beanstalk, he began to climb down for dear life. Well, the Ogre didn't like trusting himself to such a ladder. While he stood there, Jack got another start.

But just then the harp cried out: "Master! Master!" and the Ogre swung himself down on to the beanstalk, which shook with his weight. By this time Jack had climbed down till he was nearly home. So he called out, "Mother! Mother! Bring me the ax, bring me the ax." And his mother came rushing out with the ax in her hand.

Jack jumped down, took the ax, and gave a chop at the beanstalk. The Ogre felt the beanstalk shake and quiver. Then Jack gave another chop with the ax, and the beanstalk began to topple over. Then the Ogre fell down and broke his crown, and the beanstalk came toppling after.

What with showing the people the singing harp, and selling the golden eggs that the hen laid, Jack and his mother soon became very rich. Jack then married a beautiful princess and they lived happily ever after.

The Sheep with the Wooden Collar

a French-Canadian folk tale
from *sashes red and blue*
by Natalie Savage Carlson

Little Jean-Baptiste LeBlanc began feeling like one big
man when he had a brother smaller than himself. The
new Nichet was not a playmate for him yet, but
Jean-Baptiste did not mind that.

He carried his little brother about in his arms. He
talked to him and sang a song to him about a gray hen
who laid her *coco*[1] in the church just for Nichet.

When all the LeBlancs went to a stay-awake party
given by the neighbors, Jean-Baptiste was made the
special watcher of the new little nest egg. Now that he
was such a big boy, he was able to stay awake later at
the parties. He was able to sing songs with the others
and listen to the exciting stories told by the old heads.
Stories about fearsome *loups garous*[2] and *lutins*[3] and
fi-follets[4].

Jean-Baptiste began wishing he could tell such stories.
He often thought about this as he rocked his little
brother or played with his pet whistler, who woke up in
the spring and still remembered how to dance.

He thought about the exciting stories as he did his
chores around the farmhouse. He was thinking about
them the day his father sent him and his dog Toutou[5] to
the river pasture to drive home the sheep.

Jean-Baptiste leaned on the woven fence that leaned
on the ground.

He watched the sheep nibbling the fresh grass and

---

1. *Coco* (koh KOH) is a childish term for an egg.
2. A *loup garou* (lou ga ROO) is a werewolf—a person in
   folklore who can change himself into a wolf.
3. A *lutin* (loo TEHN) is a goblin—a mischievous sprite or elf in
   folklore, in the form of an ugly looking dwarf.
4. A *fi-follet* (fih foh LAY) is an elf or hobgoblin.
5. Toutou (too TOO) is French for "bow-wow" or "doggie."

bleating about nothing at all. He watched the marbly-eyed gray sheep who wore a wooden collar around her neck.

"That sheep has a mind of her own," his father had said. "It is not bad for a cow or a chicken or a horse to have a mind of its own. But when a sheep has a mind of her own, she begins jumping over fences."

So the sheep with her own mind had to wear a wooden collar so she couldn't jump over the woven fence.

She had her own mind with her this late afternoon. *"Moute, moute!"* Jean-Baptiste called to the sheep.

All the other sheep were ready to follow tails home, but the one with the wooden collar had her own idea. She ran back and forth across the pasture, lifting her hoofs and lifting her tail.

Toutou was right behind her, nipping at her hoofs as they went up and down. First she ran away to the north. Then she turned east. Finally she turned south and followed the other sheep to the road.

Jean-Baptiste thought about this as he and Toutou walked in the dust of the sheep.

"Bê! Bê!" bleated the other sheep in a chorus, as if they were singing a round.

But the sheep with the mind of her own didn't sing one "bê." She tossed her wooden collar. She lifted her hoofs and she lifted her tail. She ran along by herself.

Jean-Baptiste decided to make his story about her. As his worn moccasins scuffed in the dusty sheep tracks, his mind made up the story. He could hardly wait to get home to tell it to his father.

He didn't have to wait that long. Luc Boulanger came driving his two-wheeled cart toward them. When he met the sheep, he saw that he couldn't go any farther until they were past him. So he stopped his horse.

The sheep on the right wanted to pass him on the left. The sheep on the left wanted to pass him on the right. They bumped into each other and followed tails around Luc Boulanger's cart. They made two streams of wool, as if the cart were a canoe in the middle.

"Bê! Bê!" bleated the sheep following tails.

But the sheep with the wooden collar didn't say a single "bê." She just lifted her hoofs and lifted her tail until she came to Luc Boulanger's horse. Then she dropped her hoofs and dropped her tail. She would not go any farther. Luc Boulanger snapped at her with his whip, but that only frightened his horse.

"That is a stubborn sheep you have there," said Luc to Jean-Baptiste.

Jean-Baptiste put his hands in his pockets and looked up at Luc.

"She is a very strange sheep also," said the boy. "I did not think I would get her this close to home. She wouldn't leave the pasture with the other sheep. She ran

north and grew as big as a yearling calf. She turned
east and grew as big as a horse. She turned south and
grew as big as a house. So, believe me, the other sheep
and I started to run down this road as fast as our feet
would take us. And Toutou ran too. He was afraid of
that sheep as big as a house."

Luc Boulanger's eyes were almost as big as his ears at
this tale. He backed his horse way over to the side of
the road. He squeezed himself into the farthest end of
the seat as the sheep with the wooden collar went by,
lifting her hoofs and lifting her tail.

Jean-Baptiste and Toutou drove the sheep up the
LeBlanc lane to the barn. The boy opened the door and
the dog drove the sheep through it.

Then the little boy kicked up his moccasins like a
frolicky lamb himself. He ran to find his father. He
found him mending a broken hoe near the back door.

Jean-Baptiste put his hands in his pockets and looked
up into his father's face.

"Papa," he said, "something very strange happened
today."

"Did that sheep jump the fence even with the wooden collar on her neck?" asked Jean LeBlanc.

"No, Papa, it was stranger than that," said the boy. "When I went with Toutou to get the sheep, she tried to run away from us. She ran north and grew big as a yearling calf. She turned east and grew big as a horse. She turned south and grew big as a house. It really stretched my eyes, Papa."

"My faith," cried Jean LeBlanc. "The sheep is bewitched. I always thought there was something strange about a sheep having a mind of her own. Do not go near her alone."

All the other LeBlancs were told about the sheep.

"She ran north and got big as a yearling calf," repeated Jean-Baptiste, with his hands in his pockets. "She turned east and grew big as a horse. She turned south and grew big as a house."

The little LeBlancs began to howl.

"She is a *loup garou*," cried Marie-Elaine. "We are living on a farm with a *loup garou*."

"The *lutin* must be riding her," cried Pierre-Paul.

Mamma was sitting in the rocking chair feeding the new Nichet some gruel. She held the baby closer so that the sheep could not get him.

"Poush!" said Grandmère. "A sheep is a sheep. How could a stupid sheep grow big as a horse or a house? Come here, Jean-Baptiste. Let me feel your forehead. Perhaps you have a fever."

But no one listened to Grandmère because a fever is a dull thing while a bewitched sheep is an exciting one.

Luc Boulanger came over next day. He came on his own two legs. He kept looking uneasily toward the barn.

"Jean LeBlanc," he said, "that sheep with the wooden collar stood in the road and stared at my horse. Now my horse has gone lame."

Jean LeBlanc was sorry about the lame horse. He offered Luc Boulanger the loan of his own horse.

It wasn't long before Luc Boulanger was back again.

"Jean LeBlanc," he said, "you remember how your

bewitched sheep nibbled a leaf off my apple tree as she went down the road this morning. Now all the leaves are turning brown and I think the tree will die."

Jean LeBlanc could sympathize with his neighbor about the apple tree. What is as good as an apple baked in pastry or eaten raw in its own red skin?

"I will see that you get some of my apples this summer," he offered.

Everyone told Jean LeBlanc what to do about his sheep. But Jaco Pichet, the butcher, had the best cure for a bewitched sheep.

"Bring her to my place," he said, "and I will butcher her. She will no longer run north and east and south. And I have yet to see the mutton chops that grew any bigger after they left the butcher's scales."

Jean LeBlanc agreed that this was the best thing to do about the sheep with the wooden collar.

He asked Jean-Baptiste to help him get her to the butcher because all the sheep were used to the little boy.

Jean-Baptiste helped his father unfasten the wooden collar from the sheep's neck. He helped tie her hoofs together. He helped lift her into the two-wheeled cart. And all the time that Jean-Baptiste was helping, he had an unhappy look on his small face.

He sat quietly beside his father on the seat of the cart. His head hung low. He did not ask any questions.

"Bê-e-e," cried the sheep in protest, as the cart rode over a stone in the road.

Jean-Baptiste could not stand himself any longer. "Papa," he said in a low voice, "I have something to tell you."

"Did you forget to close the barn door?" asked his father.

"Worse than that, Papa," said Jean-Baptiste. "The sheep we are taking to the butcher did not go north and get big as a yearling calf. She did not turn east and grow big as a horse. She did not turn south and grow big as a house. She only ran around in the pasture lifting her hoofs and lifting her tail."

Jean LeBlanc pulled on the reins. The horse stopped and the cart stopped.

"Jean-Baptiste," said his father sternly, "you have been telling one big untruth about the poor sheep."

The boy miserably nodded his head. "I don't want her to go to the butcher, Papa," he said. "She never does anything wrong but jump over fences. And she looks so gay when she runs across the pasture lifting her hoofs and lifting her tail."

Jean LeBlanc turned the horse around. The road was not wide so he had to make the horse and cart go back and forth several times before they were headed for home again.

"It is a wicked thing to tell an untruth, Jean-Baptiste," said his father.

The boy nodded some more. Then he fell into deep thought. As usual his deep thought was followed by questions.

"Papa," asked Jean-Baptiste, "is it an untruth when

the old heads say that they were chased by the *loup garou?* Was Michel Meloche telling a big untruth when he said that a boat of ghostly fishermen went flying through the clouds?"

Jean LeBlanc suddenly became very busy with his horse. He yelled at her and jerked at the reins as if she were running away.

"My faith, must you spill us into the ditch?" shouted Jean LeBlanc, although his horse wasn't doing anything but jogging along in the middle of the road.

Jean-Baptiste sat waiting for his father's answer.

His father settled back into the seat again. He changed the reins from one hand to the other. He cracked the whip over the horse's back. *Flic, flac.* Then he smiled wisely at his little son.

"The old heads and Michel Meloche do not tell untruths, my little cabbage," he said. "They tell stories."

"What is the difference between an untruth and a story?" asked the boy.

"Ho, ho, there is a great difference," said his father, getting busy with the horse again.

"But what *is* the difference, Papa?" insisted Jean-Baptiste.

The wise look which the boy knew so well crossed his father's face again.

"The difference is in the way one tells it," said Jean LeBlanc. "When a man tells an untruth, he stands still with his hands in his pockets and his eyes in one place. But when a man tells a story he waves his arms *ça* [6] and rolls his eyes *ça*. Then all the people know that they can believe it or not—as they wish."

Jean-Baptiste was satisfied with this explanation.

Soon they were home and the boy had to confess to the whole family that he had told an untruth about the sheep with the wooden collar.

Mamma scolded him and the other children were

---

6. *ça* (sah) is French for "so."

ashamed of him. But Grandmère could understand exactly how it had happened.

She took Jean-Baptiste into her own room and did some more explaining about untruths and stories.

"It is like this, Jean-Baptiste," she said. "You have often heard that when our people first came to Canada, they were surrounded by dangers. There were hostile Indians and fierce animals and new sicknesses. But these dangers were not enough for people as strong and brave as ours. They needed more dangers so they made up *loups garous* and *lutins* and *fi-follets*. And all the other creatures that only people as smart as ours could think up." Grandmère patted the little boy's head. Then she untied the strings of the round black cap on her head. "But as far as your old Grandmère can see, they are only fancy untruths," she added tartly.

So the sheep had her wooden collar put on her neck again and she went back to the pasture with the others.

Everything was explained to the neighbors in a way which did not shame little Jean-Baptiste. It was done at the Boulangers' stay-awake party one pleasant summer evening. It was a gay fete, with tables full of food and floors full of dancing feet and children.

Old Pierre Boulanger played his violin and even the grandmères danced to that.

When all the feet were tired of dancing and half of the children were asleep, Luc Boulanger waved his hands for quiet.

"A story," he cried. "Who will tell us an exciting story?"

Then Jean LeBlanc rose to his feet and proudly looked down at his next-to-the-littlest son.

"Jean-Baptiste has a story," he announced. "Only a few have heard it so far, but tonight he will tell it to everyone."

He stood the boy on a chair so everyone could see him. Then he sat down again.

Jean-Baptiste blinked like a little owl pulled out of its

tree hole. Then he began to wave his arms *ça* and roll
his eyes *ça*.

"We have a strange sheep," he said. "Only last week
she did a marvelous thing which I saw with my own
eyes. I had gone to the pasture with Toutou, our dog, to
bring home the sheep."

Faster waved Jean-Baptiste's arms *ça* and faster
rolled his eyes *ça*.

"But the sheep with the wooden collar would not
follow the other sheep. She ran away from us. She went
north and grew big as a yearling calf. She turned east
and grew big as a horse. She turned south and grew big
as a house. Then there was a terrible clap of thunder,
and lightning flashed all around that great sheep. Fire
came out of her eyes and—my faith, I ran home then."

Everyone laughed and clapped. Luc Boulanger laughed
and clapped the loudest. He knew now that the sheep
was not really bewitched. Everyone knew that there was
nothing wrong with the sheep with the wooden collar
except that she liked to jump over fences.

Luc Boulanger patted Jean-Baptiste on the back. "You
are one fine storyteller," he said. "When you get big,
you will be as good as old Michel Meloche."

Favorite Fables

The Lion and the Mouse

by Aesop

Once when a Lion was asleep, a little Mouse began running up and down upon him. This soon wakened the Lion. Angry at being disturbed, the Lion placed his huge paw upon the little Mouse and opened his big jaws to swallow him.

"Pardon, O King," cried the little Mouse. "If you will let me go, I shall never forget your kindness. Who knows but what I may be able to do you a good turn one day."

The Lion was so amused at the idea of the Mouse being able to help him, that he lifted up his paw and let him go.

Some time later, the little Mouse heard the Lion roaring angrily. When he went to see what the trouble was, he found the Lion caught in a hunter's net. Remembering his promise, the little Mouse set to work nibbling at the ropes with his sharp teeth. And before long, the Lion was able to crawl out of the net.

Little friends may prove great friends.

The Crow
and the Pitcher

by Aesop

A crow, half-dead with thirst, came upon a pitcher which
had once been full of water. But when the Crow put his
beak into the pitcher, he found that there was only a
little water left in it. Try as he would, he could not
reach far enough down to get a drink.

Then a thought came to him. He took a pebble and
dropped it into the pitcher. Then he took another pebble
and dropped it into the pitcher. Before long, he could see
the water rising higher and higher. After casting a few
more pebbles, he was able to get a drink.

Little by little does the trick.

The Hare and the Tortoise

by Aesop

The Hare was once boasting of his speed before the other animals. "I have never yet been beaten," said he. "When I put forth my full speed, I can run faster than any of you. I challenge anyone here to race with me."

The Tortoise said quietly, "I accept your challenge."

"That is a good joke," said the Hare. "I could dance round you all the way."

"Keep your boasting till you've won," answered the Tortoise. "Shall we race?"

So a course was fixed and a start was made. The Hare darted out of sight at once. Soon, knowing that he was far ahead, he stopped to have a nap.

Meanwhile, the Tortoise plodded along, slowly and steadily. When the Hare awoke from his nap, he saw the Tortoise nearing the finish line. The Hare leaped up and ran as fast as he could. But he was not in time. The Tortoise won the race.

Slow and steady wins the race.

The Shepherd Boy and the Wolf

by Aesop

There was once a young shepherd boy who watched over his sheep every day. While the sheep ate grass, he passed the time by seeing how far he could throw a rock, or by looking at the clouds to see how many animal shapes he could find.

He liked his job well enough, but he longed for a little excitement. So, one day he decided to play a trick on the people of the village.

"Wolf! Wolf!" he shouted as loud as he could.

Hearing the shepherd boy's cry, the people in the village picked up pitchforks and clubs and ran to help the boy save his sheep. When they arrived, they saw no wolf. They saw only the shepherd boy, doubled up with laughter.

"I fooled you. I fooled you," he said.

The people thought this was a very bad joke, indeed. They warned the boy not to call again, unless he really saw a wolf.

The next week, the boy again played his trick on the villagers.

"Wolf! Wolf!" he cried out.

Once again, the people ran to his aid, and once again, they found no wolf—only the boy, laughing at them.

The next day, a wolf really did come down from the hills to help itself to a few fat sheep. "Wolf! Wolf!" yelled the shepherd boy with all the power in his lungs.

The people of the village heard his shouts for help and smiled. "He's trying to trick us again," they said, "but this time we won't be fooled."

Finally, the boy stopped shouting. He knew the villagers didn't believe him. He knew they wouldn't come. All he could do was stand back and watch the wolf kill his sheep.

People who tell lies are seldom believed,
even when they tell the truth.

The Ant and the Dove

by Aesop

An Ant was speeding along on its three pairs of legs when, suddenly, it stopped.

"I'm thirsty," the Ant said aloud.

"Why don't you get a drink of water from the brook?" cooed a Dove perched in a nearby tree. "The brook is close by. Just be careful you don't fall in."

The Ant sped to the brook and began to drink. But a sudden gust of wind blew the Ant into the water.

"Help!" cried the Ant, "I'm drowning!"

The Dove knew it had to act quickly to save the Ant. With its beak, the Dove broke a twig from the tree. Then the Dove flew over the brook and dropped the twig to the Ant. The Ant climbed onto the twig and floated safely ashore.

Not long afterward, the Ant saw a Hunter. He was setting a trap to catch the Dove. The Dove began to fly toward the trap.

The Ant knew it had to act quickly to save the Dove. So the Ant opened its strong jaws and bit the bare ankle of the Hunter.

"Ouch!" the Hunter cried.

The Dove heard the Hunter and flew away to safety.

One good turn deserves another.

144

The Dog and the Bone

by Aesop

It so happened that a dog had a fine bone and was carrying it home to chew on in peace. On his way, he had to go across a plank over a stream.

As he walked across the plank, he looked down and saw his reflection in the water. Thinking that it was another dog with another bone, he made up his mind to have that bone, too. But when he snapped at his reflection, his own bone fell into the water and was lost forever.

The greedy often lose what they have.

The Foolish, Timid Rabbit

a Jataka Tale from India
retold by Ellen C. Babbitt

Once upon a time, a Rabbit was asleep under a
palmtree.

All at once he woke up, and thought: "What if the
world should break up! What then would become of me?"

At that moment, some Monkeys dropped a coconut. It
fell down on the ground just back of the Rabbit.

Hearing the noise, the Rabbit said to himself: "The
earth is all breaking up!"

And he jumped up and ran just as fast as he could,
without even looking back to see what made the noise.

Another Rabbit saw him running, and called after
him, "What are you running so fast for?"

"Don't ask me!" he cried.

But the other Rabbit ran after him, begging to know
what was the matter.

Then the first Rabbit said: "Don't you know? The earth is all breaking up!"

And on he ran, and the second Rabbit ran with him.

The next Rabbit they met ran with them when he heard that the earth was all breaking up.

One Rabbit after another joined them, until there were hundreds of Rabbits running as fast as they could go.

They passed a Deer, calling out to him that the earth was all breaking up. The Deer then ran with them.

The Deer called to a Fox to come along because the earth was all breaking up.

On and on they ran, and an Elephant joined them.

At last the Lion saw the animals running, and heard their cry that the earth was all breaking up.

He thought there must be some mistake, so he ran to the foot of a hill in front of them and roared three times.

This stopped them, for they knew the voice of the King of Beasts, and they feared him.

"Why are you running so fast?" asked the Lion.

"Oh, King Lion," they answered him, "the earth is all breaking up!"

"Who saw it breaking up?" asked the Lion.

"I didn't," said the Elephant. "Ask the Fox—he told me about it."

"I didn't," said the Fox.

"The Rabbits told me about it," said the Deer.

One after another of the Rabbits said: "I did not see it, but another Rabbit told me about it."

At last the Lion came to the Rabbit who had first said the earth was all breaking up.

"Is it true that the earth is all breaking up?" the Lion asked.

"Yes, O Lion, it is," said the Rabbit. "I was asleep under a palmtree. I woke up and thought, 'What would become of me if the earth should all break up?' At that very moment, I heard the sound of the earth breaking up, and I ran away."

"Then," said the Lion, "you and I will go back to the place where the earth began to break up, and see what is the matter."

So the Lion put the little Rabbit on his back, and away they went like the wind. The other animals waited for them at the foot of the hill.

The Rabbit told the Lion when they were near the place where he slept, and the Lion saw just where the Rabbit had been sleeping.

He saw, too, the coconut that had fallen to the ground near by. Then the Lion said to the Rabbit, "It must have been the sound of the coconut falling to the ground that you heard. You foolish Rabbit!"

And the Lion ran back to the other animals, and told them all about it.

If it had not been for the wise King of Beasts, they might be running still.

The Monkey and the Crocodile

a Jataka Tale from India
retold by Ellen C. Babbitt

A Monkey lived in a great tree on a river bank. In the river there were many Crocodiles.

A Crocodile watched the Monkeys for a long time, and one day she said to her son: "My son, get one of those Monkeys for me. I want the heart of a Monkey to eat."

"How am I to catch a Monkey?" asked the little Crocodile. "I do not travel on land, and the Monkey does not go into the water."

"Put your wits to work, and you'll find a way," said the mother.

And the little Crocodile thought and thought.

At last he said to himself: "I know what I'll do. I'll get that Monkey that lives in a big tree on the river bank. He will wish to go across the river to the island where the fruit is so ripe."

So the Crocodile swam to the tree where the Monkey lived. But he was a stupid Crocodile.

"Oh, Monkey," he called, "come with me over to the island where the fruit is so ripe."

"How can I go with you?" asked the Monkey. "I do not swim."

"No—but I do. I will take you over on my back," said the Crocodile.

The Monkey was greedy, and wanted the ripe fruit, so he jumped down on the Crocodile's back.

"Off we go!" said the Crocodile.

"This is a fine ride you are giving me!" said the Monkey.

"Do you think so? Well, how do you like this?" asked the Crocodile, diving.

"Oh, don't!" cried the Monkey, as he went under the water. He was afraid to let go, and he did not know what to do under the water.

When the Crocodile came up, the Monkey sputtered and choked. "Why did you take me underwater, Crocodile?" he asked.

"I am going to kill you by keeping you underwater," answered the Crocodile. "My mother wants the heart of a Monkey to eat, and I'm going to take yours to her."

"I wish you had told me you wanted my heart," said the Monkey, "then I might have brought it with me."

"How queer!" said the stupid Crocodile. "Do you mean to say that you left your heart back there in the tree?"

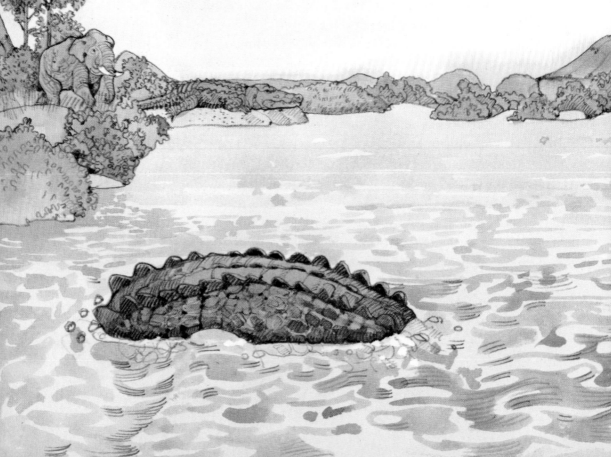

"That is what I mean," said the Monkey. "If you want my heart, we must go back to the tree and get it. But we are so near the island where the ripe fruit is, please take me there first."

"No, Monkey," said the Crocodile, "I'll take you straight back to your tree. Never mind the ripe fruit. Get your heart and bring it to me at once. Then we'll see about going to the island."

"Very well," said the Monkey.

But no sooner had he jumped onto the bank of the river than—whisk! up he ran into the tree.

From the topmost branches he called down to the Crocodile in the water below:

"My heart is way up here! If you want it, come for it, come for it!"

How the Turtle Saved His Own Life

a Jataka Tale from India
retold by Ellen C. Babbitt

A king once had a lake made in the courtyard for the young princes to play in. They swam about in it, and sailed their boats and rafts on it. One day the king told them he had asked the men to put some fishes into the lake.

Off the boys ran to see the fishes. Now, along with the fishes, there was a Turtle. The boys were delighted with the fishes, but they had never seen a Turtle, and they were afraid of it, thinking it was a demon. They ran back to their father, crying, "There is a demon on the bank of the lake."

The king ordered his men to catch the demon, and to bring it to the palace. When the Turtle was brought in, the boys cried and ran away.

The king was very fond of his sons, so he ordered the men who had brought the Turtle to kill it.

"How shall we kill it?" they asked.

"Pound it to powder," said someone. "Bake it in hot coals," said another.

So one plan after another was spoken of. Then an old
man who had always been afraid of the water said:
"Throw the thing into the lake where it flows out over
the rocks into the river. Then it will surely be killed."

When the Turtle heard what the old man said, he
thrust out his head and asked: "Friend, what have I
done that you should do such a dreadful thing as that to
me? The other plans were bad enough, but to throw me
into the lake! Don't speak of such a cruel thing!"

When the king heard what the Turtle said, he told his
men to take the Turtle at once and throw it into the
lake.

The Turtle laughed to himself as he slid away down
the river to his old home. "Good!" he said, "those people
do not know how safe I am in the water!"

Stories & Poems

The Velveteen Rabbit

from *The Velveteen Rabbit or How Toys Become Real*
by Margery Williams

There was once a velveteen rabbit, and in the beginning
he was really splendid. He was fat and bunchy, as a
rabbit should be; his coat was spotted brown and white,
he had real thread whiskers, and his ears were lined
with pink sateen. On Christmas morning, when he sat
wedged in the top of the Boy's stocking, with a sprig of
holly between his paws, the effect was charming.

There were other things in the stocking, nuts and
oranges and a toy engine, and chocolate almonds and a
clockwork mouse, but the Rabbit was quite the best of
all. For at least two hours the Boy loved him, and then
Aunts and Uncles came to dinner, and there was a great
rustling of tissue paper and unwrapping of parcels, and
in the excitement of looking at all the new presents the
Velveteen Rabbit was forgotten.

For a long time he lived in the toy cupboard or on the nursery floor, and no one thought very much about him. He was naturally shy, and being only made of velveteen, some of the more expensive toys quite snubbed him. The mechanical toys were very superior, and looked down upon every one else; they were full of modern ideas, and pretended they were real. The model boat, who had lived through two seasons and lost most of his paint, caught the tone from them and never missed an opportunity of referring to his rigging in technical terms. The Rabbit could not claim to be a model of anything, for he didn't know that real rabbits existed; he thought they were all stuffed with sawdust like himself, and he understood that sawdust was quite out-of-date and should never be mentioned in modern circles. Even Timothy, the jointed wooden lion, who was made by the disabled soldiers, and should have had broader views, put on airs and pretended he was connected with Government. Between them all the poor little Rabbit was made to feel himself very insignificant and commonplace, and the only person who was kind to him at all was the Skin Horse.

The Skin Horse had lived longer in the nursery than any of the others. He was so old that his brown coat was bald in patches and showed the seams underneath, and most of the hairs in his tail had been pulled out to string bead necklaces. He was wise, for he had seen a long succession of mechanical toys arrive to boast and swagger, and by-and-by break their mainsprings and pass away, and he knew that they were only toys, and would never turn into anything else. For nursery magic is very strange and wonderful, and only those playthings that are old and wise and experienced like the Skin Horse understand all about it.

"What is REAL?" asked the Rabbit one day, when they were lying side by side near the nursery fender, before Nana came to tidy the room. "Does it mean having things that buzz inside you and a stick-out handle?"

"Real isn't how you are made," said the Skin Horse.

"It's a thing that happens to you. When a child loves you for a long, long time, not just to play with, but REALLY loves you, then you become Real."

"Does it hurt?" asked the Rabbit.

"Sometimes," said the Skin Horse, for he was always truthful. "When you are Real you don't mind being hurt."

"Does it happen all at once, like being wound up," he asked, "or bit by bit?"

"It doesn't happen all at once," said the Skin Horse. "You become. It takes a long time. That's why it doesn't often happen to people who break easily, or have sharp edges, or who have to be carefully kept. Generally, by the time you are Real, most of your hair has been loved off, and your eyes drop out and you get loose in the joints and very shabby. But these things don't matter at all, because once you are Real you can't be ugly, except to people who don't understand."

"I suppose *you* are Real?" said the Rabbit. And then he wished he had not said it, for he thought the Skin Horse might be sensitive. But the Skin Horse only smiled.

"The Boy's Uncle made me Real," he said. "That was a great many years ago; but once you are Real you can't become unreal again. It lasts for always."

The Rabbit sighed. He thought it would be a long time before this magic called Real happened to him. He longed to become Real, to know what it felt like; and yet the idea of growing shabby and losing his eyes and whiskers was rather sad. He wished that he could become it without these uncomfortable things happening to him.

There was a person called Nana who ruled the nursery. Sometimes she took no notice of the playthings lying about, and sometimes, for no reason whatever, she went swooping about like a great wind and hustled them away in cupboards. She called this "tidying up," and the playthings all hated it, especially the tin ones. The Rabbit didn't mind it so much, for wherever he was thrown he came down soft.

One evening, when the Boy was going to bed, he couldn't find the china dog that always slept with him. Nana was in a hurry, and it was too much trouble to hunt for china dogs at bedtime, so she simply looked about her, and seeing that the toy cupboard door stood open, she made a swoop.

"Here," she said, "take your old Bunny! He'll do to sleep with you!" And she dragged the Rabbit out by one ear, and put him into the Boy's arms.

That night, and for many night after, the Velveteen Rabbit slept in the Boy's bed. At first he found it rather uncomfortable, for the Boy hugged him very tight, and sometimes he rolled over on him, and sometimes he pushed him so far under the pillow that the Rabbit could scarcely breathe. And he missed, too, those long moonlight hours in the nursery, when all the house was silent, and his talks with the Skin Horse. But very soon he grew to like it, for the Boy used to talk to him, and made nice tunnels for him under the bedclothes that he said were like the burrows the real rabbits lived in. And they had splendid games together, in whispers, when

Nana had gone away to her supper and left the night light burning on the mantelpiece. And when the Boy dropped off to sleep, the Rabbit would snuggle down close under his little warm chin and dream, with the Boy's hands clasped close round him all night long.

And so time went on, and the little Rabbit was very happy—so happy that he never noticed how his beautiful velveteen fur was getting shabbier and shabbier, and his tail coming unsewn, and all the pink rubbed off his nose where the Boy had kissed him.

Spring came, and they had long days in the garden,

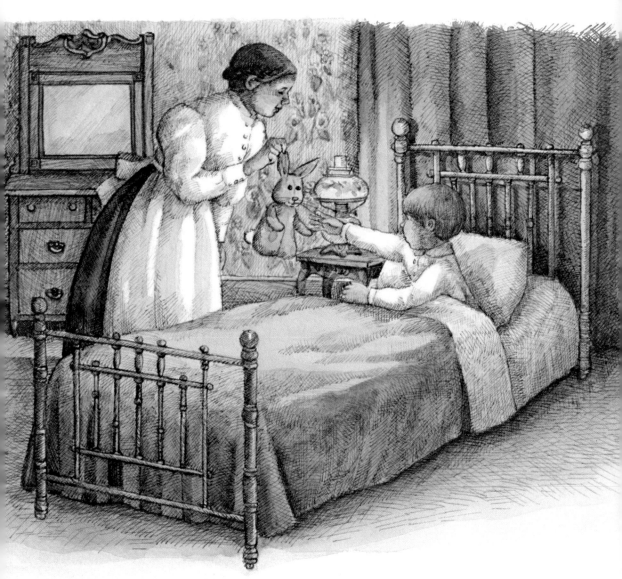

for wherever the Boy went the Rabbit went too. He had rides in the wheelbarrow, and picnics on the grass, and lovely fairy huts built for him under the raspberry canes behind the flower border. And once, when the Boy was called away suddenly to go out to tea, the Rabbit was left out on the lawn until long after dusk, and Nana had to come and look for him with the candle because the Boy couldn't go to sleep unless he was there. He was wet through with the dew and quite earthy from diving into the burrows the Boy had made for him in the flower bed, and Nana grumbled as she rubbed him off with a corner of her apron.

"You must have your old Bunny!" she said. "Fancy all that fuss for a toy!"

The Boy sat up in bed and stretched out his hands.

"Give me my Bunny!" he said. "You mustn't say that. He isn't a toy. He's REAL!"

When the little Rabbit heard that he was happy, for he knew that what the Skin Horse had said was true at last. The nursery magic had happened to him, and he was a toy no longer. He was Real. The Boy himself had said it.

That night he was almost too happy to sleep, and so much love stirred in his little sawdust heart that it almost burst. And into his boot-button eyes, that had long ago lost their polish, there came a look of wisdom and beauty, so that even Nana noticed it next morning when she picked him up, and said, "I declare if that old Bunny hasn't got quite a knowing expression!"

The little Rabbit is now real to the boy, but a great deal more happens to him before he *truly* becomes real—as you will discover when you read the rest of *The Velveteen Rabbit*. And if you liked this story, you will also like *Theodore* by Edward Ormondroyd, which is about an old teddy bear and the little girl who loves him.

Bed in Summer

by Robert Louis Stevenson

In winter I get up at night
And dress by yellow candlelight.
In summer, quite the other way,
I have to go to bed by day.

I have to go to bed and see
The birds still hopping on the tree,
Or hear the grown-up people's feet
Still going past me in the street.

And does it not seem hard to you,
When all the sky is clear and blue,
And I should like so much to play,
To have to go to bed by day?

My Teddy Bear

by Marchette Chute

A teddy bear is a faithful friend.
You can pick him up at either end.
His fur is the color of breakfast toast,
And he's always there when you need him most.

Otherwise
by Aileen Fisher

There must be magic,
Otherwise,
How could day turn to night,

And how could sailboats,
Otherwise,
Go sailing out of sight,

And how could peanuts,
Otherwise,
Be covered up so tight?

Hippity Hop to Bed
by Leroy F. Jackson

O it's hippity hop to bed!
I'd rather sit up instead.
But when father says "must,"
There's nothing but just
Go hippity hop to bed.

163

Furry Bear

by A. A. Milne

If I were a bear,
   And a big bear too,
I shouldn't much care
   If it froze or snew;
I shouldn't much mind
   If it snowed or friz—
I'd be all fur-lined
   With a coat like his!

For I'd have fur boots and a brown fur wrap,
And brown fur knickers and a big fur cap.
I'd have a fur muffle-ruff to cover my jaws,
And brown fur mittens on my big brown paws.
With a big brown furry-down up to my head,
I'd sleep all the winter in a big fur bed.

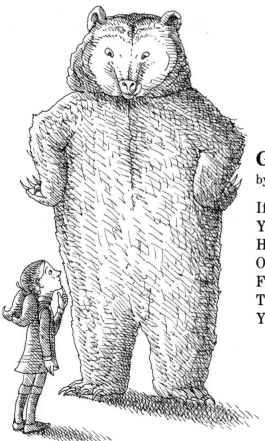

Grizzly Bear

by Mary Austin

If you ever, ever, ever meet a grizzly bear,
You must never, never, never ask him *wher*
He is going,
Or *what* he is doing;
For if you ever, ever dare
To stop a grizzly bear,
You will never meet *another* grizzly bear.

Whistle for Willie

by Ezra Jack Keats
illustrations by Ezra Jack Keats

Oh, how Peter wished he could whistle!

He saw a boy playing with his dog. Whenever the boy whistled, the dog ran straight to him.

Peter tried and tried to whistle, but he couldn't. So instead he began to turn himself around—around and around he whirled ... faster and faster.... When he stopped, everything turned down ... and up ... and up ... and down ... and around and around.

Peter saw his dog, Willie, coming. Quick as a wink, he hid in an empty carton lying on the sidewalk.

"Wouldn't it be funny if I whistled?" Peter thought. "Willie would stop and look all around to see who it was."

Peter tried again to whistle—but still he couldn't. So Willie just walked on.

Peter got out of the carton and started home. On the way he took some colored chalks out of his pocket and drew a long, long line right up to his door. He stood there and tried to whistle again. He blew till his cheeks were tired. But nothing happened.

He went into his house and put on his father's old hat to make himself feel more grown-up. He looked into the mirror to practice whistling. Still no whistle!

When his mother saw what he was doing, Peter pretended that he was his father. He said, "I've come home early today, dear. Is Peter here?"

His mother answered, "Why no, he's outside with Willie."

"Well, I'll go out and look for them," said Peter.

First he walked along a crack in the sidewalk. Then he tried to run away from his shadow. He jumped off his shadow. But when he landed they were together again. He came to the corner where the carton was, and who should he see but Willie!

Peter scrambled under the carton. He blew and blew and blew. Suddenly—out came a real whistle!

Willie stopped and looked around to see who it was.

"It's me," Peter shouted, and stood up. Willie raced straight to him.

Peter ran home to show his father and mother what he could do. They loved Peter's whistling. So did Willie.

Peter's mother asked him and Willie to go on an errand to the grocery store. He whistled all the way there, and he whistled all the way home.

Ezra Jack Keats has written other picture books in which Peter appears, including *The Snowy Day* and *Letter to Amy*. Girls will especially like his book *Jennie's Hat*, which is the story of a little girl who wants a beautiful flowered hat and what happens when she gets a very plain one.

The Little Whistler
by Frances M. Frost

My mother whistled softly,
My father whistled bravely,
My brother whistled merrily,
And I tried all day long!
I blew my breath inwards,
I blew my breath outwards,
But all you heard was breath blowing
And not a bit of song!

But today I heard a bluebird,
A happy, young, and new bird,
Whistling in the apple tree—
He'd just discovered how!
Then quick I blew my breath in,
And gay I blew my breath out,
And sudden I blew three wild notes—
And I can whistle now!

Whistles
by Dorothy Aldis

I want to learn to whistle.
I've always wanted to.
I fix my mouth to do it but
The whistle won't come through.

I think perhaps it's stuck, and so
I try it once again.
Can people swallow whistles?
Where is my whistle then?

Dogs
by Marchette Chute

The dogs I know
Have many shapes.
For some are big and tall,
And some are long,
And some are thin,
And some are fat and small.
And some are little bits of fluff
And have no shape at all.

My Dog
by Marchette Chute

His nose is short and scrubby;
   His ears hang rather low;
And he always brings the stick back,
   No matter how far you throw.

He gets spanked rather often
   For things he shouldn't do,
Like lying-on-beds, and barking,
   And eating up shoes when they're new.

He always wants to be going
   Where he isn't supposed to go.
He tracks up the house when it's snowing—
   Oh, puppy, I love you so.

After a Bath

by Aileen Fisher

After my bath
I try, try, try
to wipe myself
till I'm dry, dry, dry.

Hands to wipe
and fingers and toes
and two wet legs
and a shiny nose.

Just think how much
less time I'd take
if I were a dog
and could shake, shake, shake.

The Hairy Dog

by Herbert Asquith

My dog's so furry I've not seen
His face for years and years:
His eyes are buried out of sight,
I only guess his ears.

When people ask me for his breed,
I do not know or care:
He has the beauty of them all
Hidden beneath his hair.

The Tale of Peter Rabbit

by Beatrix Potter
illustrations by Beatrix Potter

Once upon a time there were four little Rabbits, and
their names were—

>Flopsy,
>>Mopsy,
>>>Cotton-tail,
>>>>and Peter.

They lived with their Mother in a sand-bank, underneath the root of a very big fir-tree.

"Now, my dears," said old Mrs. Rabbit one morning, "you may go into the fields or down the lane, but don't go into Mr. McGregor's garden: your Father had an accident there; he was put in a pie by Mrs. McGregor.

"Now run along, and don't get into mischief. I am going out."

Then old Mrs. Rabbit took a basket and her umbrella, and went through the wood to the baker's. She bought a loaf of brown bread and five currant buns.

Flopsy, Mopsy, and Cotton-tail, who were good little bunnies, went down the lane to gather blackberries.

But Peter, who was very naughty, ran straight away to Mr. McGregor's garden, and squeezed under the gate!

First he ate some lettuces and some French beans; and then he ate some radishes. And then, feeling rather sick, he went to look for some parsley.

But round the end of a cucumber frame, whom should he meet but Mr. McGregor!

Mr. McGregor was on his hands and knees planting out young cabbages, but he jumped up and ran after Peter, waving a rake and calling out, "Stop thief!"

Peter was most dreadfully frightened; he rushed all over the garden, for he had forgotten the way back to the gate.

He lost one of his shoes among the cabbages, and the other shoe amongst the potatoes.

After losing them, he ran on four legs and went faster, so that I think he might have got away altogether if he had not unfortunately run into a gooseberry net, and got caught by the large buttons on his jacket. It was a blue jacket with brass buttons, quite new.

Peter gave himself up for lost, and shed big tears; but his sobs were overheard by some friendly sparrows, who flew to him in great excitement, and implored him to exert himself.

Mr. McGregor came up with a sieve, which he

intended to pop upon the top of Peter; but Peter
wriggled out just in time, leaving his jacket behind him.

And rushed into the tool-shed, and jumped into a can.
It would have been a beautiful thing to hide in, if it had
not had so much water in it.

Mr. McGregor was quite sure that Peter was
somewhere in the tool-shed, perhaps hidden underneath
a flower-pot. He began to turn them over carefully,
looking under each.

Presently Peter sneezed—"Kertyschoo!" Mr. McGregor
was after him in no time, and tried to put his foot upon
Peter, who jumped out of a window, upsetting three
plants. The window was too small for Mr. McGregor, and
he was tired of running after Peter. He went back to his
work.

Peter sat down to rest; he was out of breath and
trembling with fright, and he had not the least idea
which way to go. Also he was very damp with sitting in
that can.

After a time he began to wander about, going
lippity—lippity—not very fast, and looking all around.

He found a door in a wall; but it was locked, and there
was no room for a fat little rabbit to squeeze
underneath.

An old mouse was running in and out over the stone
doorstep, carrying peas and beans to her family in the
wood. Peter asked her the way to the gate, but she had
such a large pea in her mouth that she could not answer.
She only shook her head at him. Peter began to cry.

Then he tried to find his way straight across the
garden, but he became more and more puzzled.
Presently, he came to a pond where Mr. McGregor filled
his watercans. A white cat was staring at some
gold-fish; she sat very, very still, but now and then the
tip of her tail twitched as if it were alive. Peter thought
it best to go away without speaking to her; he had heard
about cats from his cousin, little Benjamin Bunny.

He went back towards the tool-shed, but suddenly,
quite close to him, he heard the noise of a

hoe—scr-r-ritch, scratch, scratch, scritch. Peter scuttered underneath the bushes. But presently, as nothing happened, he came out, and climbed upon a wheelbarrow, and peeped over. The first thing he saw was Mr. McGregor hoeing onions. His back was turned towards Peter, and beyond him was the gate!

Peter got down very quietly off the wheelbarrow, and started running as fast as he could go, along a straight walk behind some black-currant bushes.

Mr. McGregor caught sight of him at the corner, but Peter did not care. He slipped underneath the gate, and was safe at last in the wood outside the garden.

Mr. McGregor hung up the little jacket and the shoes for a scarecrow to frighten the blackbirds.

Peter never stopped running or looked behind him till he got home to the big fir-tree.

He was so tired that he flopped down upon the nice soft sand on the floor of the rabbit-hole, and shut his

eyes. His mother was busy cooking; she wondered what
he had done with his clothes. It was the second little
jacket and pair of shoes that Peter had lost in a
fortnight![1]

I am sorry to say that Peter was not very well during
the evening.

His mother put him to bed, and made some camomile
tea; and she gave a dose of it to Peter!

"One table-spoonful to be taken at bed-time."

But Flopsy, Mopsy, and Cotton-tail had bread and
milk and blackberries, for supper.

The Tale of Peter Rabbit was the first modern picture
book. Among Beatrix Potter's many other charming
books for young children are *The Tale of Benjamin
Bunny, The Tale of Jemima Puddle-Duck,* and *The
Tailor of Gloucester.*

---

1. A fortnight (short for fourteen nights) is two weeks.

There Once
Was a Puffin
by Florence Page Jaques

Oh, there once was a Puffin
Just the shape of a muffin,
And he lived on an island
In the
　bright
　　blue
　　　sea!

He ate little fishes,
That were most delicious,
And he had them for supper
And he
　had
　　them
　　　for tea.

But this poor little Puffin,
He couldn't play nothin',
For he hadn't anybody
To
　play
　　with
　　　at all.

So he sat on his island,
And he cried for awhile, and
He felt very lonely,
And he
　felt
　　very
　　　small.

Then along came the fishes,
And they said, "If you wishes,
You can have us for playmates,
Instead
　of
　　for
　　　tea!"

So they now play together,
In all sorts of weather,
And the puffin eats pancakes,
Like you
　and
　　like
　　　me.

The Little Turtle
by Vachel Lindsay

There was a little turtle.
He lived in a box.
He swam in a puddle.
He climbed on the rocks.

He snapped at a mosquito.
He snapped at a flea.
He snapped at a minnow.
And he snapped at me.

He caught the mosquito.
He caught the flea.
He caught the minnow.
But he didn't catch me.

The Monkeys and the Crocodile
by Laura E. Richards

Five little monkeys
  Swinging from a tree;
Teasing Uncle Crocodile,
  Merry as can be.
Swinging high, swinging low,
  Swinging left and right:
"Dear Uncle Crocodile,
  Come and take a bite!"

Five little monkeys
  Swinging in the air;
Heads up, tails up,
  Little do they care.
Swinging up, swinging down,
  Swinging far and near:
"Poor Uncle Crocodile,
  Aren't you hungry, dear?"

Four little monkeys
  Sitting in a tree;
Heads down, tails down,
  Dreary as can be.
Weeping loud, weeping low,
  Crying to each other:
"Wicked Uncle Crocodile
  To gobble up our brother!"

Whisky Frisky

author unknown

Whisky Frisky,
Hippity-hop
Up he goes
To the treetop!

Whirly, twirly,
Round and round,
Down he scampers
To the ground.

Furly, curly,
What a tail!
Tall as a feather,
Broad as a sail!

Where's his supper?
In the shell,
Snap, cracky,
Out it fell.

mommies

by Nikki Giovanni

MOMMIES
  make you brush your teeth
  and put your old clothes on
  and clean the room
  and call you from the playground
  and fuss at daddies and uncles
  and tuck you in at night
  and kiss you

The Reason

by Dorothy Aldis

Rabbits and squirrels
Are furry and fat,
And all of the chickens
Have feathers, and *that*
Is why when it's raining
They need not stay in
The way children do who have
Only their skin.

Pooh Goes Visiting

from *Winnie-the-Pooh*
by A. A. Milne

Young Christopher Robin and his stuffed bear,
Winnie-the-Pooh, have been favorites for years. Pooh,
also known as Edward Bear, lives in a house in the
forest. For reasons known only to Pooh, the sign over
the door to his den says, "Mr. Sanders."

⚜ ⚜ ⚜

Edward Bear, known to his friends as Winnie-the-Pooh,
or Pooh for short, was walking through the forest one
day, humming proudly to himself. He had made up a
little hum that very morning, as he was doing his
Stoutness Exercises in front of the glass: *Tra-la-la,
tra-la-la,* as he stretched up as high as he could go, and
then *Tra-la-la, tra-la—oh, help!—la,* as he tried to reach
his toes. After breakfast he had said it over and over to
himself until he had learnt it off by heart, and now he
was humming it right through, properly. It went like
this:

> *Tra-la-la, tra-la-la,*
> *Tra-la-la, tra-la-la,*
> *Rum-tum-tiddle-um-tum.*
> *Tiddle-iddle, tiddle-iddle,*
> *Tiddle-iddle, tiddle-iddle,*
> *Rum-tum-tum-tiddle-um.*

Well, he was humming this hum to himself, and
walking along gaily, wondering what everybody else was
doing, and what it felt like, being somebody else, when
suddenly he came to a sandy bank, and in the bank was
a large hole.

"Aha!" said Pooh. (*Rum-tum-tiddle-um-tum*). "If I
know anything about anything, that hole means Rabbit,"
he said, "and Rabbit means Company," he said, "and
Company means Food and Listening-to-Me-Humming
and such like. *Rum-tum-tum-tiddle-um.*"

So he bent down, put his head into the hole, and called out:

"Is anybody at home?"

There was a sudden scuffling noise from inside the hole, and then silence.

"What I said was, 'Is anybody at home?'" called out Pooh very loudly.

"No!" said a voice; and then added, "You needn't shout so loud. I heard you quite well the first time."

"Bother!" said Pooh. "Isn't there anybody here at all?"

"Nobody."

Winnie-the-Pooh took his head out of the hole, and thought for a little, and he thought to himself, "There must be somebody there, because somebody must have *said* 'Nobody.'" So he put his head back in the hole, and said:

"Hallo, Rabbit, isn't that you?"

"No," said Rabbit, in a different sort of voice this time.

"But isn't that Rabbit's voice?"

"I don't *think* so," said Rabbit. "It isn't *meant* to be."

"Oh!" said Pooh.

He took his head out of the hole, and had another think, and then he put it back, and said:

"Well, could you very kindly tell me where Rabbit is?"

"He has gone to see his friend Pooh Bear, who is a great friend of his."

"But this *is* Me!" said Bear, very much surprised.

"What sort of Me?"

"Pooh Bear."

"Are you sure?" said Rabbit, still more surprised.

"Quite, quite sure," said Pooh.

"Oh, well, then, come in."

So Pooh pushed and pushed and pushed his way through the hole, and at last he got in.

"You were quite right," said Rabbit, looking at him all over. "It *is* you. Glad to see you."

"Who did you think it was?"

"Well, I wasn't sure. You know how it is in the Forest.

One can't have *anybody* coming into one's house. One
has to be *careful*. What about a mouthful of something?"

Pooh always liked a little something at eleven o'clock
in the morning, and he was very glad to see Rabbit
getting out the plates and mugs; and when Rabbit said,
"Honey or condensed milk with your bread?" he was so
excited that he said, "Both," and then, so as not to seem
greedy, he added, "But don't bother about the bread,
please." And for a long time after that he said nothing
... until at last, humming to himself in a rather sticky
voice, he got up, shook Rabbit lovingly by the paw, and
said that he must be going on.

"Must you?" said Rabbit politely.

"Well," said Pooh, "I could stay a little longer if it—if
you——" and he tried very hard to look in the direction
of the larder.

"As a matter of fact," said Rabbit, "I was going out
myself directly."

"Oh, well, then, I'll be going on. Good-bye."

"Well, good-bye, if you're sure you won't have any
more."

"*Is* there any more?" asked Pooh quickly.

Rabbit took the covers off the dishes, and said, "No, there wasn't."

"I thought not," said Pooh, nodding to himself. "Well, good-bye. I must be going on."

So he started to climb out of the hole. He pulled with his front paws, and pushed with his back paws, and in a

little while his nose was out in the open again . . . and then his ears . . . and then his front paws . . . and then his shoulders . . . and then——

"Oh, help!" said Pooh. "I'd better go back."

"Oh, bother!" said Pooh. "I shall have to go on."

"I can't do either!" said Pooh. "Oh, help *and* bother!"

Now by this time Rabbit wanted to go for a walk too, and finding the front door full, he went out by the back door, and came around to Pooh, and looked at him.

"Hallo, are you stuck?" he asked.

"N-no," said Pooh carelessly. "Just resting and thinking and humming to myself."

"Here, give us a paw."

Pooh Bear stretched out a paw, and Rabbit pulled and pulled and pulled . . . .

"Ow!" cried Pooh. "You're hurting!"

"The fact is," said Rabbit, "you're stuck."

"It all comes," said Pooh crossly, "of not having front doors big enough."

"It all comes," said Rabbit sternly, "of eating too much. I thought at the time," said Rabbit, "only I didn't like to say anything," said Rabbit, "that one of us was eating too much," said Rabbit, "and I knew it wasn't *me*," he said. "Well, well, I shall go and fetch Christopher Robin.

Christopher Robin lived at the other end of the Forest, and when he came back with Rabbit, and saw the front half of Pooh, he said, "Silly old Bear," in such a loving voice that everybody felt quite hopeful again.

"I was just beginning to think," said Bear, sniffing slightly, "that Rabbit might never be able to use his front door again. And I should *hate* that," he said.

"So should I," said Rabbit.

"Use his front door again?" said Christopher Robin. "Of course he'll use his front door again."

"Good," said Rabbit.

"If we can't pull you out, Pooh, we might push you back."

Rabbit scratched his whiskers thoughtfully, and pointed out that, when once Pooh was pushed back, he was back, and of course nobody was more glad to see Pooh than *he* was, still there it was, some lived in trees and some lived underground, and——

"You mean I'd *never* get out?" said Pooh.

"I mean," said Rabbit, "that having got so far, it seems a pity to waste it."

Christopher Robin nodded.

"Then there's only one thing to be done," he said. "We shall have to wait for you to get thin again."

"How long does getting thin take?" asked Pooh anxiously.

"About a week, I should think."

"But I can't stay here for a *week!*"

"You can *stay* here all right, silly old Bear. It's getting you out which is so difficult."

"We'll read to you," said Rabbit cheerfully. "And I hope it won't snow," he added. "And I say, old fellow, you're taking up a good deal of room in my house—*do* you mind if I use your back legs as a towel-horse? Because, I mean, there they are—doing nothing—and it would be very convenient just to hang the towels on them."

"A week!" said Pooh gloomily. *"What about meals?"*

"I'm afraid no meals," said Christopher Robin, "because of getting thin quicker. But we *will* read to you."

Bear began to sigh, and then found he couldn't because he was so tightly stuck; and a tear rolled down his eye, as he said:

"Then would you read a Sustaining Book, such as would help and comfort a Wedged Bear in Great Tightness?"

So for a week Christopher Robin read that sort of book at the North end of Pooh, and Rabbit hung his washing on the South end ... and in between Bear felt himself getting slenderer and slenderer. And at the end of the week Christopher Robin said, *"Now!"*

So he took hold of Pooh's front paws and Rabbit took hold of Christopher Robin, and all Rabbit's friends and relations took hold of Rabbit, and they all pulled together....

And for a long time Pooh only said *"Ow!"* . . .

And *"Oh!"* . . .

And then, all of a sudden, he said *"Pop!"* just as if a cork were coming out of a bottle.

And Christopher Robin and Rabbit and all Rabbit's friends and relations went head-over-heels backwards . . . and on the top of them came Winnie-the-Pooh—free!

So, with a nod of thanks to his friends, he went on with his walk through the forest, humming proudly to himself. But, Christopher Robin looked after him lovingly, and said to himself, "Silly old Bear!"

You can enjoy more of Pooh Bear's adventures, and meet more of his friends, in A. A. Milne's books *Winnie-the-Pooh* and *The House at Pooh Corner*.

The Kangaroo
by Elizabeth Coatsworth

It is a curious thing that you
don't wish to be a kangaroo,
   to hop hop hop
   and never stop
the whole day long and the whole night, too!

to hop across Australian plains
with tails that sweep behind like trains
   and small front paws
   and pointed jaws
and pale neat coats to shed the rains.

If skies be blue, if skies be gray,
they bound in the same graceful way
   into dim space
   at such a pace
that where they go there's none to say!

Nature Note
by Arthur Guiterman

Undoubtedly the Kangaroos
   Have fun;
They hop because they do not choose
   To run.

The Rabbit
by Elizabeth Madox Roberts

When they said the time to hide was mine,
I hid back under a thick grapevine.

And while I was still for the time to pass,
A little gray thing came out of the grass.

He hopped his way through the melon bed
And sat down close by a cabbage head.

He sat down close where I could see,
And his big still eyes looked hard at me,

His big eyes bursting out of the rim,
And I looked back very hard at him.

Hoppity
by A. A. Milne

Christopher Robin goes
Hoppity, hoppity,

Hoppity, hoppity, hop.
Whenever I tell him
Politely to stop it, he
Says he can't possibly stop.

If he stopped hopping, he couldn't go anywhere,
Poor little Christopher
Couldn't go anywhere ...
That's why he *always* goes
Hoppity, hoppity,
Hoppity,
Hoppity,
Hop.

The Duel

by Eugene Field

The gingham dog and the calico cat
Side by side on the table sat;
'Twas half-past twelve, and (what do you think!)
Nor one nor t'other had slept a wink!
   The old Dutch clock and the Chinese plate
   Appeared to know as sure as fate
There was going to be a terrible spat.
   (I wasn't there; I simply state
   What was told to me by the Chinese plate!)

The gingham dog went, "Bow-wow-wow!"
And the calico cat replied, "Mee-ow!"
The air was littered, and hour or so,
With bits of gingham and calico,
   While the old Dutch clock in the chimney-place
   Up with its hands before its face,
For it always dreaded a family row!
   (Now mind: I'm only telling you
   What the old Dutch clock declares is true!)

The Chinese plate looked very blue,
And wailed, "Oh, dear! what shall we do!"
But the gingham dog and the calico cat
Wallowed this way and tumbled that,
   Employing every tooth and claw
   In the awfullest way you ever saw—
And, oh! how the gingham and calico flew!
   (Don't fancy I exaggerate—
   I got my news from the Chinese plate!)

Next morning, where the two had sat,
They found no trace of dog or cat;
And some folks think unto this day
That burglars stole that pair away!
 But the truth about the cat and pup
 Is this: they ate each other up!
Now what do you really think of that!
 (*The old Dutch clock it told me so,*
 And that is how I came to know.)

Pinocchio

from *The Adventures of Pinocchio* by Carlo Collodi
translated from the Italian by Carol Della Chiesa

When Mastro Cherry the carpenter found a piece of
wood that laughed and talked, he gave it to his good
friend Geppetto. The kindly old Geppetto took the
wood home, for he wanted to carve a marionette that
would dance and turn somersaults. And so begins the
story of the famous—and very naughty—Pinocchio.

⚜ ⚜ ⚜

Little as Geppetto's house was, it was neat and
comfortable. It was a small room on the ground floor,
with a tiny window under the stairway. The furniture
could not have been much simpler: a very old chair, a
rickety old bed, and a tumble-down table. A fireplace
full of burning logs was painted on the wall opposite the
door. Over the fire, there was painted a pot full of
something which kept boiling happily away and sending
up clouds of what looked like real steam.

As soon as he reached home, Geppetto took his tools
and began to cut and shape the wood into a marionette.

"What shall I call him?" he said to himself. "I think

I'll call him *Pinocchio*. This name will make his fortune. I knew a whole family of Pinocchi once—Pinocchio the father, Pinocchia the mother, and Pinocchi the children—and they were all lucky. The richest of them begged for his living."

After choosing the name for his marionette, Geppetto set seriously to work to make the hair, the forehead, the eyes. Fancy his surprise when he noticed that these eyes moved, and then stared fixedly at him. Geppetto, seeing this, felt insulted and said in a grieved tone:

"Ugly wooden eyes, why do you stare so?"

There was no answer.

After the eyes, Geppetto made the nose, which began to stretch as soon as finished. It stretched and stretched and stretched till it became so long it seemed endless.

Poor Geppetto kept cutting it and cutting it, but the more he cut, the longer grew that impertinent nose. In despair he let it alone.

Next he made the mouth.

No sooner was it finished than it began to laugh and poke fun at him.

"Stop laughing!" said Geppetto angrily; but he might as well have spoken to the wall.

"Stop laughing, I say!" he roared in a voice of thunder. The mouth stopped laughing, but stuck out a long tongue.

Not wishing to start an argument, Geppetto made believe he saw nothing and went on with his work.

After the mouth, he made the chin, then the neck, the shoulders, the stomach, the arms, and the hands.

As he was about to put the last touches on the finger tips, Geppetto felt his wig being pulled off. He glanced up and what did he see? His yellow wig was in the marionette's hand. "Pinocchio, give me my wig!"

But instead of giving it back, Pinocchio put it on his own head, which was half swallowed up in it.

At that unexpected trick, Geppetto became very sad and downcast, more so than he had ever been before.

"Pinocchio, you wicked boy!" he cried out. "You are not yet finished, and you start out by being impudent to your poor old father. Very bad, my son, very bad!"

And he wiped away a tear.

The legs and feet still had to be made. As soon as they were done, Geppetto felt a sharp kick on his nose.

"I deserve it!" he said to himself. "I should have thought of this before I made him. Now it's too late!"

He took hold of the marionette under the arms and put him on the floor to teach him to walk.

Pinocchio's legs were so stiff that he could not move them, and Geppetto held his hand and showed him how to put out one foot after the other.

When his legs were limbered up, Pinocchio started walking by himself and ran all around the room. He came to the open door, and with one leap he was out into the street. Away he flew!

Poor Geppetto ran after him but was unable to catch him, for Pinocchio ran in leaps and bounds, his two wooden feet, as they beat on the stones of the street, making as much noise as twenty peasants in wooden shoes.

"Catch him! Catch him!" Geppetto kept shouting. But the people in the street, seeing a wooden marionette

running like the wind, stood still to stare and to laugh until they cried.

At last, by sheer luck, a policeman happened along who, hearing all that noise, thought that it might be a runaway colt, and stood bravely in the middle of the street, with legs wide apart, firmly resolved to stop it and prevent any trouble.

Pinocchio saw the policeman from afar and tried his best to escape between the legs of the big fellow, but without success.

The policeman grabbed him by the nose (it was an extremely long one and seemed made on purpose for that very thing) and returned him to Mastro Geppetto.

The little old man wanted to pull Pinocchio's ears. Think how he felt when, upon searching for them, he discovered that he had forgotten to make them!

All he could do was to seize Pinocchio by the back of the neck and take him home. As he was doing so, he shook him two or three times and said to him angrily:

"We're going home now. When we get home, then we'll settle this matter!"

Pinocchio, on hearing this, threw himself on the ground and refused to take another step. One person after another gathered around the two.

Some said one thing, some another.

"Poor marionette," called out a man. "I am not surprised he doesn't want to go home. Geppetto, no doubt, will beat him unmercifully, he is so mean and cruel!"

"Geppetto looks like a good man," added another, "but with boys he's a real tyrant. If we leave that poor marionette in his hands he may tear him to pieces!"

They said so much that, finally, the policeman ended matters by setting Pinocchio at liberty and dragging Geppetto to prison. The poor old fellow did not know how to defend himself, but wept and wailed like a child and said between his sobs:

"Ungrateful boy! To think I tried so hard to make you a well-behaved marionette! I deserve it, however! I should have given the matter more thought."

Very little time did it take to get poor old Geppetto to prison. In the meantime that rascal, Pinocchio, free now from the clutches of the policeman, was running wildly across fields and meadows, taking one short cut after another toward home. In his wild flight, he leaped over brambles and bushes, and across brooks and ponds, as if he were a goat or a hare chased by hounds.

On reaching home, he found the house door half open. He slipped into the room, locked the door, and threw himself on the floor, happy at his escape. But, as night came on, a queer, empty feeling at the pit of his stomach reminded the marionette that he had eaten nothing as yet.

A boy's appetite grows very fast, and in a few moments the queer, empty feeling had become hunger, and the hunger grew bigger and bigger, until soon he was as ravenous as a bear.

Poor Pinocchio ran to the fireplace where the pot was boiling and stretched out his hand to take the cover off, but to his amazement the pot was only painted! Think how he felt! His long nose became at least two inches longer.

He ran about the room, dug in all the boxes and drawers, and even looked under the bed in search of a piece of bread, hard though it might be, or a cooky, or perhaps a bit of fish. A bone left by a dog would have tasted good to him! But he found nothing.

And meanwhile his hunger grew and grew. The only relief poor Pinocchio had was to yawn; and he certainly did yawn. Soon he became dizzy and faint.

He wept and wailed to himself: "It was wrong of me to disobey Father and to run away from home. If he were here now, I wouldn't be so hungry! Oh, how horrible it is to be hungry!"

Suddenly he saw, among the sweepings in a corner, something round and white that looked very much like a hen's egg. In a jiffy he pounced upon it. It was an egg.

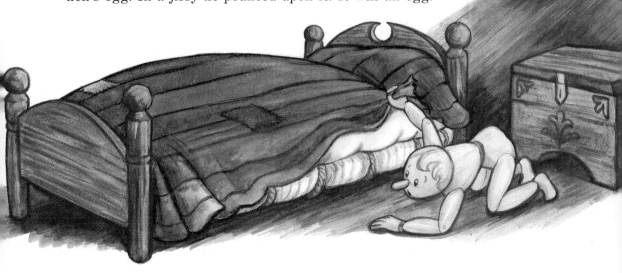

The marionette's joy knew no bounds. It is impossible to describe it, you must picture it to yourself. Certain that he was dreaming, he turned the egg over and over in his hands, fondled it, kissed it, and talked to it:

"And now, how shall I cook you? Shall I make an omelet? No, it is better to fry you in a pan! Or shall I drink you? No, the best way is to fry you in the pan. You will taste better."

No sooner said than done. He placed a little pan over
a foot warmer full of hot coals. In the pan, instead of oil
or butter, he poured a little water. As soon as the water
started to boil—tac!—he broke the eggshell. But in place
of the white and the yolk of the egg, a little yellow
chick, fluffy and gay and smiling, escaped from it.
Bowing politely to Pinocchio, he said to him:

"Many, many thanks, indeed, Mr. Pinocchio, for
having saved me the trouble of breaking my shell!
Good-by and good luck to you and remember me to the
family!"

With these words he spread out his wings and,
darting to the open window, he flew away into space till
he was out of sight.

The poor marionette stood as if turned to stone, with
wide eyes, open mouth, and the empty halves of the
eggshell in his hands. When he came to himself, he
began to cry and shriek at the top of his lungs,
stamping his feet on the ground and wailing all the
while: "If I had not run away from home and if Father

were here now, I should not be dying of hunger. Oh, how horrible it is to be hungry!"

And as his stomach kept grumbling more than ever and he had nothing to quiet it with, he thought of going out for a walk to the nearby village, in the hope of finding some charitable person who might give him a bit of bread.

Pinocchio hated the dark street, but he was so hungry that, in spite of it, he ran out of the house. The night was pitch-black. It thundered, and bright flashes of lightning now and again shot across the sky, turning it into a sea of fire. An angry wind blew cold and raised dense clouds of dust, while the trees shook and moaned in a weird way.

Pinocchio was greatly afraid of thunder and lightning, but the hunger he felt was far greater than his fear. In a dozen leaps and bounds, he came to the village, tired out, puffing like a whale, and with his tongue hanging.

The whole village was dark and deserted. The stores were closed, the doors, the windows. In the streets, not even a dog could be seen.

Pinocchio, in desperation, ran up to a doorway, threw himself upon the bell, and pulled it wildly, saying to himself, "Someone will surely answer that!"

He was right. An old man in a nightcap opened the window and looked out. He called down angrily, "What do you want at this hour of night?"

"Will you be good enough to give me a bit of bread? I am hungry."

"Wait a minute and I'll come right back," answered the old fellow, thinking he had to deal with one of those boys who love to roam around at night ringing people's bells while they are peacefully asleep.

After a minute or two, the same voice cried, "Get under the window and hold out your hat!"

Pinocchio had no hat, but he managed to get under the window just in time to feel a shower of ice-cold water pour down on his poor wooden head, his shoulders, and over his whole body.

He returned home as wet as a rat, and tired out from weariness and hunger.

As he no longer had any strength left with which to stand, he sat down on a little stool and put his two feet on the stove to dry them.

There he fell asleep, and while he slept, his wooden

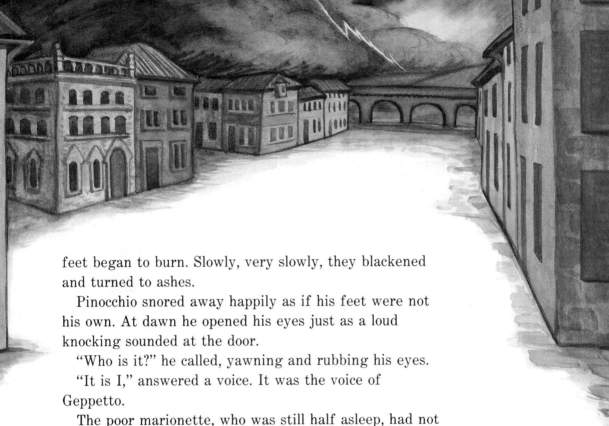

feet began to burn. Slowly, very slowly, they blackened and turned to ashes.

Pinocchio snored away happily as if his feet were not his own. At dawn he opened his eyes just as a loud knocking sounded at the door.

"Who is it?" he called, yawning and rubbing his eyes.

"It is I," answered a voice. It was the voice of Geppetto.

The poor marionette, who was still half asleep, had not yet found out that his two feet were burned and gone. As soon as he heard his father's voice, he jumped up from his seat to open the door, but, as he did so, he staggered and fell headlong to the floor.

In falling, he made as much noise as a sack of wood falling from the fifth story of a house.

"Open the door for me!" Geppetto shouted from the street.

"Father, dear Father, I can't," answered the marionette in despair, crying and rolling on the floor.

"Why can't you?"

"Because someone has eaten my feet."

"And who has eaten them?"

"The cat," answered Pinocchio, seeing that little animal busily playing with some shavings in the corner of the room.

"Open! I say," repeated Geppetto, "or I'll give you a sound whipping when I get in."

"Father, believe me, I can't stand up. Oh, dear! Oh, dear! I shall have to walk on my knees all my life."

Geppetto, thinking that all these tears and cries were only other pranks of the marionette, climbed up the side of the house and went in through the window.

At first he was very angry, but on seeing Pinocchio stretched out on the floor and really without feet, he felt very sad and sorrowful. Picking him up from the floor, he fondled and caressed him, talking to him while the tears ran down his cheeks: "My little Pinocchio, my dear little Pinocchio! How did you burn your feet?"

"I don't know, Father, but believe me, the night has been a terrible one and I shall remember it as long as I live. The thunder was so noisy and the lightning so bright—and I was hungry. I put the pan on the coals,

but the chick flew away and said, 'I'll see you again! Remember me to the family.' And my hunger grew, and I went out, and the old man with a nightcap looked out of the window and threw water on me, and I came home and put my feet on the stove to dry them because I was still hungry, and I fell asleep and now my feet are gone but my hunger isn't! Oh!—Oh!—Oh!" And poor Pinocchio began to scream and cry so loudly that he could be heard for miles around.

Geppetto, who had understood nothing of all that jumbled talk except that the marionette was hungry, felt sorry for him and, pulling three pears out of his pocket, offered them to him, saying, "These three pears were for my breakfast, but I give them to you gladly. Eat them and stop weeping."

"If you want me to eat them, please peel them for me."

"Peel them?" asked Geppetto, very much surprised. "I should never have thought, dear boy of mine, that you were so dainty and fussy about your food. Bad, very bad! In this world, even as children, we must accustom ourselves to eat of everything, for we never know what life may hold in store for us!"

"You may be right," answered Pinocchio, "but I will not eat the pears if they are not peeled. I don't like them."

And good old Geppetto took out a knife, peeled the three pears, and put the skins in a row on the table.

Pinocchio ate one pear in a twinkling and started to throw the core away, but Geppetto held his arm.

"Oh, no, don't throw it away! Everything in this world may be of some use!"

"But the core I will not eat!" cried Pinocchio in an angry tone.

"Who knows?" repeated Geppetto calmly.

And later the three cores were placed on the table next to the skins.

Pinocchio had eaten the three pears, or rather devoured them. Then he yawned and wailed, "I'm still hungry."

"But I have no more to give you."

"Really, nothing—nothing?"

"I have only these three cores and these skins."

"Very well, then," said Pinocchio, "if there is nothing else I'll eat them."

At first he made a wry face, but, one after another, the skins and the cores disappeared.

"Ah! Now I feel fine!" he said after eating the last one.

"You see," observed Geppetto, "that I was right when I told you that one must not be too fussy and too dainty about food. My dear, we never know what life may have in store for us!"

The marionette, as soon as his hunger was appeased, started to grumble and cry that he wanted a new pair of feet. But Mastro Geppetto, in order to punish him for his mischief, let him alone the whole morning. After dinner he said to him, "Why should I make your feet over again? To see you run away from home once more?"

"I promise you," answered the marionette, sobbing, "that from now on I'll be good—"

"Boys always promise that when they want something," said Geppetto.

"I promise to go to school every day, to study, and to succeed—"

"Boys always sing that song when they want their own will."

"But I am not like other boys! I am better than all of them and I always tell the truth. I promise you, Father, that I'll learn a trade, and I'll be the comfort and support of your old age."

Geppetto, though trying to look very stern, felt his eyes fill with tears and his heart soften when he saw Pinocchio so unhappy. He said no more, but taking his tools and two pieces of wood, he set to work diligently.

In less than an hour the feet were finished, two slender, nimble little feet, strong and quick, modeled as if by an artist's hands.

"Close your eyes and sleep!" Geppetto then said to the marionette.

Pinocchio closed his eyes and pretended to be asleep, while Geppetto stuck on the two feet with a bit of glue melted in an eggshell, doing his work so well that the joint could hardly be seen.

As soon as the marionette felt his new feet, he gave one leap from the table and started to skip and jump around, as if he had lost his head from very joy.

"To show you how grateful I am to you, Father, I'll go to school now. But to go to school I need a suit of clothes."

Geppetto did not have a penny in his pocket, so he made his son a little suit of flowered paper, a pair of shoes from the bark of a tree, and a tiny cap from a bit of dough.

Pinocchio ran to look at himself in a bowl of water, and he felt so happy that he said proudly, "Now I look like a gentleman."

"Truly," answered Geppetto. "But remember that fine clothes do not make the man unless they be neat and clean."

"Very true," answered Pinocchio, "but, in order to go to school, I still need something very important."

"What is it?"

"An ABC book."

"To be sure! But how shall we get it?"

"That's easy. We'll go to a bookstore and buy it."

"And the money?"

"I have none."

"Neither have I," said the old man sadly.

Pinocchio, although a happy boy always, became sad and downcast at these words. When poverty shows itself, even mischievous boys understand what it means.

"What does it matter, after all?" cried Geppetto all at once, as he jumped up from his chair. Putting on his old coat, full of darns and patches, he ran out of the house without another word.

After a while he returned. In his hands he had the

ABC book for his son, but the old coat was gone. The poor fellow was in his shirt sleeves and the day was cold.

"Where's your coat, Father?"

"I have sold it."

"Why did you sell your coat?"

"It was too warm."

Pinocchio understood the answer in a twinkling, and, unable to restrain his tears, he jumped on his father's neck and kissed him over and over.

Pinocchio, whose nose grew longer every time he told a lie, was never good for very long. But after many exciting adventures, which you can read about in *The Adventures of Pinocchio*, he learns that a good marionette can become a real boy. Another fine story about a wooden doll is *Hitty: Her First Hundred Years* by Rachel Field.

Jump or Jiggle
by Evelyn Beyer

Frogs jump
Caterpillars hump

Worms wiggle
Bugs jiggle

Rabbits hop
Horses clop

Snakes slide
Sea gulls glide

Mice creep
Deer leap

Puppies bounce
Kittens pounce

Lions stalk—
But—
I walk!

Walking
by Grace Glaubitz

When Daddy
Walks
With Jean and me,
We have a
Lot of fun
'Cause we can't
Walk as fast
As he,
Unless we
Skip and
Run!
I stretch,
And stretch
My legs so far,
I nearly slip
And fall—
But how
Does Daddy
Take such steps?
He doesn't stretch
At all!

I Speak,
I Say,
I Talk

by Arnold L. Shapiro

Cats purr.
Lions roar.
Owls hoot.
Bears snore.
Crickets creak.
Mice squeak.
Sheep baa.
But I SPEAK!

Monkeys chatter.
Cows moo.
Ducks quack.
Doves coo.
Pigs squeal.
Horses neigh.
Chickens cluck.
But I SAY!

Flies hum.
Dogs growl.
Bats screech.
Coyotes howl.
Frogs croak.
Parrots squawk.
Bees buzz.
But I TALK!

Ducks' Ditty
by Kenneth Grahame

All along the backwater,
　Through the rushes tall,
Ducks are a-dabbling,
　Up tails all!

Ducks' tails, drakes' tails,
　Yellow feet a-quiver,
Yellow bills all out of sight
　Busy in the river!

Slushy green undergrowth
　Where the roaches swim—
Here we keep our larder,
　Cool and full and dim.

Everyone for what he likes!
　We like to be
Heads down, tails up,
　Dabbling free!

High in the blue above
　Swifts whirl and call—
We are down a-dabbling,
　Up tails all!

Mrs. Peck-Pigeon
by Eleanor Farjeon

Mrs. Peck-Pigeon
Is picking for bread,
Bob—bob—bob
Goes her little round head.
Tame as a pussycat
In the street,
Step—step—step
Go her little red feet.
With her little red feet
And her little round head,
Mrs. Peck-Pigeon
Goes picking for bread.

210

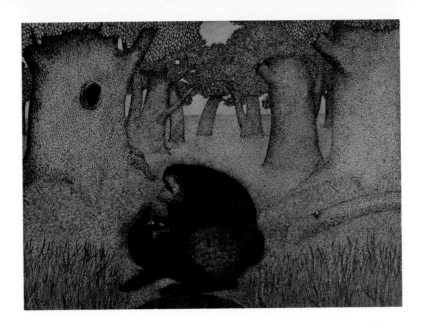

The Bunyip
of Berkeley's Creek

by Jenny Wagner
illustrations by Ron Brooks

Late one night, for no particular reason, something
stirred in the black mud at the bottom of Berkeley's
Creek.

The fish swam away in fright, and the night birds in
the trees hid their heads under their wings. When they
looked again, something very large and very muddy was
sitting on the bank.

"What am I?" it murmured. "What am I, what am I,
what am I?" And the night birds quickly hid their heads
under their wings again.

In the morning the thing was still sitting there,
scraping the mud off itself to see what was underneath.

"What am I?" it kept saying. "What am I?" But the
night birds were all asleep.

A passing platypus solved the problem. "You are a
bunyip," he said.[1]

---

1. A bunyip is a legendary Australian animal.

"Bunyip," murmured the bunyip contentedly.
"Bunyip." Then he sat up straight and called out. "What
do I look like?" But the platypus had dived into the
creek. "Am I handsome?" called the bunyip. "Am I?" But
nobody answered him, and the bunyip went on sitting
there for a long time, lost in thought.

Presently a wallaby came by to drink at the creek.

"What do bunyips look like?" asked the bunyip.

"Horrible," said the wallaby. "They have webbed feet,
and feathers."

"Fine, handsome feathers," said the bunyip hopefully.

"Horrible feathers," said the wallaby firmly, and
finished her drink and hopped off.

"Handsome webbed feet?" called the bunyip, but there
was no answer. The bunyip sighed and walked off to
find someone else.

There was a rustling in the bushes behind him, and

suddenly an emu shot past. "Wait!" called the bunyip,
running after him. "What do bunyips look like?"

The emu stopped and considered. "They have fur," he
said at last, "and tails."

"How many tails?" asked the bunyip.

"One to each bunyip," replied the emu.

"Fine, handsome tails," said the bunyip.

"Horrible tails," said the emu. "And even more
horrible fur." And he settled his feathers and crouched
down low, and streaked off into the distance.

The bunyip wandered sadly along the creek. "Will
someone tell me what bunyips look like?" he said, to
anyone who would listen.

But there was no answer.

Further along the creek he met a man. The man was
busy with a notebook and pencil, and did not look at the
bunyip. "Sh," he said, "I'm busy."

The bunyip waited for a long time, and then he said,
very slowly and clearly, "Can you please tell me what
bunyips look like?"

"Yes," said the man, without looking up. "Bunyips
don't look like anything."

"Like nothing?" said the bunyip.

"Like nothing at all," said the man.

"Are you sure?" said the bunyip.

"Quite sure," said the man, and looked right through
him. "Bunyips simply don't exist."

The bunyip was shaken. Then he sighed a long, deep
sigh. "What a pity," he murmured. "What a pity, what a
pity." And he walked slowly back to his waterhole. Then
he fished his belongings out of the water, packed them
in his bunyip bag, and walked away. No one saw him go.

The bunyip walked all day, and just as the sun was
setting he came to a quiet, still billabong. [2] "This will

---

2. A billabong is a pond or small lake.

do," said the bunyip himself. "No one can see me here. I can be as handsome as I like." And he unpacked his bag, and laid his bunyip comb and mirror out on the sand, and put his billy [3] on to boil. No one saw him and no one spoke to him.

But late that night, for no particular reason, something stirred in the black mud at the bottom of the billabong. The bunyip put his comb down in surprise, and stared. Something very large and very muddy was sitting on the bank.

"What am I?" it murmured. "What am I, what am I?"

The bunyip jumped up in delight. "You are a bunyip!" he shouted.

"Am I? Am I really?" asked the other bunyip; and then, "What do I look like?"

"You look just like me," said the bunyip happily. And he lent her his mirror to prove it.

---

3. A billy is a can for cooking over an open fire.

The Elephant
by Hilaire Belloc

When people call this beast to mind,
They marvel more and more
At such a *little* tail behind,
So LARGE a trunk before.

Holding Hands
by Lenore M. Link

Elephants walking
Along the trails

Are holding hands
By holding tails.

Trunks and tails
Are handy things

When elephants walk
In circus rings.

Elephants work
And elephants play

And elephants walk
And feel so gay.

And when they walk—
It never fails

They're holding hands
By holding tails.

Moon-in-Water

by Ivy O. Eastwick

Three Wise Men of Gotham
thought the Moon was cheese
and tried to fish it out
of the river—if you please!
but all the little tadpoles
trilled a little tune:
"You'll never, never catch it—
it's the Moon!
            Moon!
                  MOON!"

Stars

by Rhoda W. Bacmeister

Bright stars, light stars,
Shining-in-the-night stars,
Little twinkly, winkly stars,
Deep in the sky!

Yellow stars, red stars,
Shine-when-I'm-in-bed stars,
Oh how many blinky stars,
Far, far away!

The Star

by Jane Taylor

Twinkle, twinkle, little star,
How I wonder what you are,
Up above the world so high,
Like a diamond in the sky.

When the blazing sun is set,
And the grass with dew is wet,
Then you show your little light,
Twinkle, twinkle, all the night.

Alice in Wonderland

from *Alice's Adventures in Wonderland*
by Lewis Carroll

The author invented this story for a little girl named
Alice Liddell and her two sisters. He told it to them
while drifting down a river on a golden afternoon in
summer more than a hundred years ago. It has been
a favorite ever since.

1: Down the Rabbit-Hole

Alice was beginning to get very tired of sitting by her
sister on the bank, and of having nothing to do: once or
twice she had peeped into the book her sister was
reading, but it had no pictures or conversations in it,
"and what is the use of a book," thought Alice, "without
pictures or conversations?"

So she was considering, in her own mind (as well as
she could, for the hot day made her feel very sleepy and
stupid), whether the pleasure of making a daisy-chain
would be worth the trouble of getting up and picking
the daisies, when suddenly a white rabbit with pink eyes
ran close by her.

There was nothing so *very* remarkable in that; nor did Alice think it so *very* much out of the way to hear the Rabbit say to itself, "Oh dear! Oh dear! I shall be too late!" (when she thought it over afterwards, it occurred to her that she ought to have wondered at this, but at the time it all seemed quite natural); but when the Rabbit actually *took a watch out of its waistcoat-pocket*, and looked at it, and then hurried on, Alice started to her feet, for it flashed across her mind that she had never before seen a rabbit with either a waistcoat-pocket, or a watch to take out of it, and, burning with curiosity, she ran across the field after it, and was just in time to see it pop down a large rabbit-hole under the hedge.

In another moment down went Alice after it, never once considering how in the world she was to get out again.

The rabbit-hole went straight on like a tunnel for some way, and then dipped suddenly down, so suddenly that Alice had not a moment to think about stopping herself before she found herself falling down what seemed to be a very deep well.

Either the well was very deep, or she fell very slowly, for she had plenty of time as she went down to look about her, and to wonder what was going to happen next. First, she tried to look down and make out what she was coming to, but it was too dark to see anything: then she looked at the sides of the well, and noticed that they were filled with cupboards and bookshelves: here and there she saw maps and pictures hung upon pegs. She took down a jar from one of the shelves as she passed: it was labeled "ORANGE MARMALADE," but to her great disappointment it was empty: she did not like to drop the jar, for fear of killing somebody underneath, so managed to put it into one of the cupboards as she fell past it.

"Well!" thought Alice to herself, "after such a fall as this, I shall think nothing of tumbling downstairs! How brave they'll all think me at home! Why, I wouldn't say

anything about it, even if I fell off the top of the house!" (Which was very likely true.)

Down, down, down. Would the fall *never* come to an end? "I wonder how many miles I've fallen by this time?" she said aloud. "I must be getting somewhere near the centre of the earth. Let me see: that would be four thousand miles down, I think—" (for, you see, Alice had learnt several things of this sort in her lessons in the schoolroom, and though this was not a *very* good opportunity for showing off her knowledge, as there was no one to listen to her, still it was good practice to say it over) "—yes, that's about the right distance—but then I wonder what Latitude or Longitude I've got to?" (Alice had not the slightest idea what Latitude was, or Longitude either, but she thought they were nice grand words to say.)

Presently she began again. "I wonder if I shall fall right *through* the earth! How funny it'll seem to come out among the people that walk with their heads downwards! The Antipathies, I think—" (she was rather glad there *was* no one listening, this time, as it didn't

sound at all the right word) "—but I shall have to ask them what the name of the country is, you know. Please, Ma'am, is this New Zealand or Australia?" (and she tried to curtsey as she spoke—fancy *curtseying* as you're falling through the air! Do you think you could manage it?) "And what an ignorant little girl she'll think me for asking! No, it'll never do to ask: perhaps I shall see it written up somewhere."

Down, down, down. There was nothing else to do, so Alice soon began talking again. "Dinah'll miss me very much to-night, I should think!" (Dinah was the cat.) "I hope they'll remember her saucer of milk at tea-time. Dinah, my dear! I wish you were down here with me! There are no mice in the air, I'm afraid, but you might catch a bat, and that's very like a mouse, you know. But do cats eat bats, I wonder?" And here Alice began to get rather sleepy, and went on saying to herself, in a dreamy sort of way, "Do cats eat bats? Do cats eat bats?" and sometimes, "Do bats eat cats?" for, you see, as she couldn't answer either question, it didn't much matter which way she put it. She felt that she was dozing off, and had just begun to dream that she was walking hand in hand with Dinah, and was saying to her, very earnestly, "Now, Dinah, tell me the truth: did you ever eat a bat?" when suddenly, thump! thump! down she came upon a heap of sticks and dry leaves, and the fall was over.

Alice was not a bit hurt, and she jumped up on to her feet in a moment: she looked up, but it was all dark overhead; before her was another long passage, and the White Rabbit was still in sight, hurrying down it. There was not a moment to be lost: away went Alice like the wind, and was just in time to hear it say, as it turned a corner, "Oh my ears and whiskers, how late it's getting!" She was close behind it when she turned the corner, but the Rabbit was no longer to be seen: she found herself in a long, low hall, which was lit up by a row of lamps hanging from the roof.

There were doors all round the hall, but they were all

locked; and when Alice had been all the way down one
side and up the other, trying every door, she walked
sadly down the middle, wondering how she was ever to
get out again.

Suddenly she came upon a little three-legged table, all
made of solid glass: there was nothing on it but a tiny
golden key, and Alice's first idea was that this might
belong to one of the doors of the hall; but, alas! either
the locks were too large, or the key was too small, but at
any rate it would not open any of them. However, on
the second time round, she came upon a low curtain she
had not noticed before, and behind it was a little door
about fifteen inches high: she tried the little golden key
in the lock, and to her great delight it fitted!

Alice opened the door and found that it led into a
small passage, not much larger than a rat-hole: she knelt
down and looked along the passage into the loveliest
garden you ever saw. How she longed to get out of that
dark hall, and wander about among those beds of bright
flowers and those cool fountains, but she could not even
get her head through the doorway; "and even if my head
would go through," thought poor Alice, "it would be of
very little use without my shoulders. Oh, how I wish I
could shut up like a telescope! I think I could, if I only
knew how to begin." For, you see, so many
out-of-the-way things had happened lately that Alice

had begun to think that very few things indeed were
really impossible.

There seemed to be no use in waiting by the little
door, so she went back to the table, half hoping she
might find another key on it, or at any rate a book of
rules for shutting people up like telescopes: this time she
found a little bottle on it ("which certainly was not here
before," said Alice), and tied round the neck of the
bottle was a paper label with the words "DRINK ME"
beautifully printed on it in large letters.

It was all very well to say "Drink me," but the wise
little Alice was not going to do *that* in a hurry. "No, I'll
look first," she said, "and see whether it's marked
'poison' or not;" for she had read several nice little
stories about children who had got burnt, and eaten up
by wild beasts, and other unpleasant things, all because
they *would* not remember the simple rules their friends
had taught them: such as, that a red-hot poker will burn
you if you hold it too long; and that, if you cut your
finger *very* deeply with a knife, it usually bleeds; and
she had never forgotten that, if you drink much from a
bottle marked "poison," it is almost certain to disagree
with you, sooner or later.

However, this bottle was *not* marked "poison," so

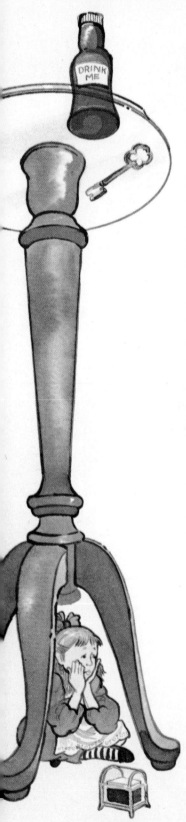

Alice ventured to taste it, and, finding it very nice (it had, in fact, a sort of mixed flavour of cherry-tart, custard, pineapple, roast turkey, toffy, and hot buttered toast), she very soon finished it off.

"What a curious feeling!" said Alice. "I must be shutting up like a telescope!"

And so it was indeed: she was now only ten inches high, and her face brightened up at the thought that she was now the right size for going through the little door into that lovely garden. First, however, she waited for a few minutes to see if she was going to shrink any further: she felt a little nervous about this; "for it might end, you know," said Alice to herself, "in my going out altogether, like a candle. I wonder what I should be like then?" And she tried to fancy what the flame of a candle looks like after the candle is blown out, for she could not remember ever having seen such a thing.

After a while, finding that nothing more happened, she decided on going into the garden at once; but, alas for poor Alice! when she got to the door, she found she had forgotten the little golden key, and when she went back to the table for it, she found she could not possibly reach it: she could see it quite plainly through the glass, and she tried her best to climb up one of the legs of the table, but it was too slippery; and when she had tired herself out with trying, the poor little thing sat down and cried.

"Come, there's no use in crying like that!" said Alice to herself, rather sharply. "I advise you to leave off this minute!" She generally gave herself very good advice (though she very seldom followed it), and sometimes she scolded herself so severely as to bring tears into her eyes; and once she remembered trying to box her own ears for having cheated herself in a game of croquet she was playing against herself, for this curious child was very fond of pretending to be two people. "But it's no use now," thought poor Alice, "to pretend to be two people! Why, there's hardly enough of me left to make *one* respectable person!"

Soon her eye fell on a little glass box that was lying under the table: she opened it, and found in it a very small cake, on which the words "EAT ME" were beautifully marked in currants. "Well, I'll eat it," said Alice, "and if it makes me grow larger, I can reach the key; and if it makes me grow smaller, I can creep under the door: so either way I'll get into the garden, and I don't care which happens!"

She ate a little bit, and said anxiously to herself, "Which way? Which way?" holding her hand on the top of her head to feel which way it was growing, and she was quite surprised to find that she remained the same size. To be sure, this is what generally happens when one eats cake; but Alice had got so much into the way of expecting nothing but out-of-the-way things to happen, that it seemed quite dull and stupid for life to go on in the common way.

So she set to work, and very soon finished off the cake.

2: The Pool of Tears

"Curiouser and curiouser!" cried Alice (she was so much surprised, that for the moment she quite forgot how to speak good English). "Now I'm opening out like the largest telescope that ever was! Good-bye, feet!" (for when she looked down at her feet, they seemed to be almost out of sight, they were getting so far off). "Oh, my poor little feet, I wonder who will put on your shoes and stockings for you now, dears? I'm sure *I* shan't be able! I shall be a great deal too far off to trouble myself about you: you must manage the best way you can—but I must be kind to them," thought Alice, "or perhaps they won't walk the way I want to go! Let me see: I'll give them a new pair of boots every Christmas."

And she went on planning to herself how she would manage it. "They must go by the carrier," she thought; "and how funny it'll seem, sending presents to one's own feet! And how odd the directions will look!

> *Alice's Right Foot, Esq.*
> *Hearthrug,*
> > *near the Fender,*
> > > *(with Alice's love).*

Oh dear, what nonsense I'm talking!"

Just at this moment her head struck against the roof of the hall: in fact she was now rather more than nine feet high, and she at once took up the little golden key and hurried off to the garden door.

Poor Alice! It was as much as she could do, lying down on one side, to look through into the garden with one eye; but to get through was more hopeless than ever: she sat down and began to cry again.

"You ought to be ashamed of yourself," said Alice, "a great girl like you," (she might well say this), "to go on crying in this way! Stop this moment, I tell you!" But she went on all the same, shedding gallons of tears, until there was a large pool all round her, about four inches deep and reaching half down the hall.

After a time she heard a little pattering of feet in the distance, and she hastily dried her eyes to see what was coming. It was the White Rabbit returning, splendidly dressed, with a pair of white kid gloves in one hand and a large fan in the other: he came trotting along in a great hurry, muttering to himself as he came, "Oh! The Duchess, the Duchess! Oh! Won't she be savage if I've kept her waiting!" Alice felt so desperate that she was ready to ask help of anyone: so, when the Rabbit came near her she began, in a low, timid voice, "If you please, Sir—" The Rabbit started violently, dropped the white

kid gloves and the fan, and scurried away into the darkness as hard as he could go.

Alice took up the fan and gloves, and, as the hall was very hot, she kept fanning herself all the time she went on talking. "Dear, dear! How queer everything is to-day! And yesterday things went on just as usual. I wonder if I've been changed in the night? Let me think: *was* I the same when I got up this morning? I almost think I can remember feeling a little different. But if I'm not the same, the next question is, 'Who in the world am I?' Ah, *that's* the great puzzle!" And she began thinking over all the children she knew that were of the same age as herself, to see if she could have been changed for any of them.

"I'm sure I'm not Ada," she said, "for her hair goes in such long ringlets, and mine doesn't go in ringlets at all; and I'm sure I can't be Mabel, for I know all sorts of things, and she, oh! she knows such a very little! Besides, *she's* she, and *I'm* I, and—oh dear, how puzzling it all is! I'll try if I know all the things I used to know. Let me see: four times five is twelve, and four times six is thirteen, and four times seven is—oh dear! I shall never get to twenty at that rate! However, the Multiplication Table doesn't signify: let's try Geography. London is the capital of Paris, and Paris is the capital of Rome, and Rome—no, *that's* all wrong, I'm certain! I must have been changed for Mabel! I'll try and say *'How doth the little—',*" and she crossed her hands on her lap, as if she were saying lessons, and began to repeat it, but her voice sounded hoarse and strange, and the words did not come the same as they used to do:—

> *"How doth the little crocodile*
> *Improve his shining tail,*
> *And pour the waters of the Nile*
> *On every golden scale!*
>
> *"How cheerfully he seems to grin,*
> *How neatly spreads his claws,*
> *And welcomes little fishes in*
> *With gently smiling jaws!"*

"I'm sure those are not the right words," said poor Alice, and her eyes filled with tears again as she went on, "I must be Mabel after all, and I shall have to go and live in that poky little house, and have next to no toys to play with, and oh! ever so many lessons to learn! No, I've made up my mind about it: if I'm Mabel, I'll stay down here! It'll be no use their putting their heads down and saying, 'Come up again, dear!' I shall only look up and say, 'Who am I, then? Tell me that first, and then, if I like being that person, I'll come up: if not, I'll stay down here till I'm somebody else'—but, oh dear!" cried Alice, with a sudden burst of tears, "I do wish they *would* put their heads down! I am so *very* tired of being all alone here!"

As she said this, she looked down at her hands, and was surprised to see that she had put on one of the Rabbit's little white kid gloves while she was talking. "How *can* I have done that?" she thought. "I must be growing small again." She got up and went to the table to measure herself by it, and found that, as nearly as she could guess, she was now about two feet high, and was going on shrinking rapidly: she soon found out that the cause of this was the fan she was holding, and she dropped it hastily, just in time to save herself from shrinking away altogether.

"That *was* a narrow escape!" said Alice, a good deal frightened at the sudden change, but very glad to find herself still in existence. "And now for the garden!" And she ran with all speed back to the little door; but, alas! the little door was shut again, and the little golden key was lying on the glass table as before, "and things are worse than ever," thought the poor child, "for I never was so small as this before, never! And I declare it's too bad, that it is!"

As she said these words her foot slipped, and in another moment, splash! she was up to her chin in salt water. Her first idea was that she had somehow fallen into the sea, "and in that case I can go back by railway," she said to herself. (Alice had been to the seaside once in her life, and had come to the general conclusion that, wherever you go to on the English coast, you find a number of bathing machines in the sea, some children digging in the sand with wooden spades, then a row of lodging-houses, and behind them a railway station.) However, she soon made out that she was in the pool of tears which she had wept when she was nine feet high.

"I wish I hadn't cried so much!" said Alice, as she swam about, trying to find her way out. "I shall be punished for it now, I suppose, by being drowned in my own tears! That *will* be a queer thing, to be sure! However, everything is queer to-day."

Just then she heard something splashing about in the pool a little way off, and she swam nearer to make out what it was: at first she thought it must be a walrus or hippopotamus, but then she remembered how small she was now, and she soon made out that it was only a mouse, that had slipped in like herself.

"Would it be of any use, now," thought Alice, "to speak to this mouse? Everything is so out-of-the-way down here, that I should think very likely it can talk: at any rate, there's no harm in trying." So she began: "O Mouse, do you know the way out of this pool? I am very tired of swimming about here, O Mouse!" (Alice thought this must be the right way of speaking to a mouse: she had never done such a thing before, but she remembered having seen, in her brother's Latin Grammar, "A mouse—of a mouse—to a mouse—a mouse—O mouse!") The mouse looked at her rather inquisitively, and seemed to her to wink with one of its little eyes, but it said nothing.

"Perhaps it doesn't understand English," thought Alice. "I daresay it's a French mouse, come over with William the Conqueror." (For, with all her knowledge of history, Alice had no very clear notion how long ago anything had happened.) So she began again: "Où est ma chatte?" which was the first sentence in her French lesson-book. The Mouse gave a sudden leap out of the water, and seemed to quiver all over with fright. "Oh, I beg your pardon!" cried Alice hastily, afraid she had

hurt the poor animal's feelings. "I quite forgot you didn't like cats."

"Not like cats!" cried the Mouse in a shrill, passionate voice. "Would *you* like cats, if you were me?"

"Well, perhaps not," said Alice in a soothing tone: "don't be angry about it. And yet I wish I could show you our cat Dinah. I think you'd take a fancy to cats, if you could only see her. She is such a dear quiet thing," Alice went on, half to herself, as she swam lazily about in the pool, "and she sits purring so nicely by the fire, licking her paws and washing her face—and she is such a nice soft thing to nurse—and she's such a capital one for catching mice—oh, I beg your pardon!" cried Alice again, for this time the Mouse was bristling all over, and she felt certain it must be really offended. "We won't talk about her any more, if you'd rather not."

"We, indeed!" cried the Mouse, who was trembling down to the end of his tail. "As if *I* would talk on such a subject! Our family always *hated* cats: nasty, low, vulgar things! Don't let me hear the name again!"

"I won't indeed!" said Alice, in a great hurry to change the subject of conversation. "Are you—are you fond—of—of dogs?" The Mouse did not answer, so Alice went on eagerly: "There is such a nice little dog near our house I should like to show you! A little bright-eyed terrier, you know, with oh, such long curly brown hair! And it'll fetch things when you throw them, and it'll sit up and beg for its dinner, and all sorts of things—I can't remember half of them—and it belongs to a farmer, you know, and he says it's so useful, it's worth a hundred pounds! He says it kills all the rats and—oh dear!" cried Alice in a sorrowful tone. "I'm afraid I've offended it again!" For the Mouse was swimming away from her as hard as it could go, and making quite a commotion in the pool as it went.

So she called softly after it, "Mouse dear! Do come back again, and we won't talk about cats, or dogs either, if you don't like them!" When the Mouse heard this, it turned round and swam slowly back to her: its face was quite pale (with passion, Alice thought), and it said, in a low, trembling voice, "Let us get to the shore, and then I'll tell you my history, and you'll understand why it is I hate cats and dogs."

It was high time to go, for the pool was getting quite crowded with the birds and animals that had fallen into it: there was a Duck and a Dodo, a Lory and an Eaglet, and several other curious creatures. Alice led the way, and the whole party swam to the shore.

Alice has many more adventures in Wonderland before she finds herself back with her sister. And her fantastic adventures are continued in another book, *Through the Looking-Glass and What Alice Found There.*

Who Is So Pretty?

by Elizabeth Coatsworth

Skitter, skatter,
Leap and squeak!
We've been dancing
Half the week.

Under the sofa,
Along the shelf,
Every mouse
Is wild as an elf.

Big round ear
And bright black eye,
Nimble and natty,
Limber and spry—

Who is so pretty,
Who is so neat,
As a little mouse dancing
On little gray feet?

Mice

by Rose Fyleman

I think mice
Are rather nice.

Their tails are long,
Their faces small,
They haven't any
Chins at all.
Their ears are pink,
Their teeth are white,
They run about
The house at night.
They nibble things
They shouldn't touch
And no one seems
To like them much.

But *I* think mice
Are nice.

The City Mouse
and the Garden Mouse
by Christina Rossetti

The city mouse lives in a house;
The garden mouse lives in a bower,
He's friendly with the frogs and toads,
And sees the pretty plants in flower.

The city mouse eats bread and cheese;
The garden mouse eats what he can;
We will not grudge him seeds and stalks,
Poor little timid furry man.

Mouse
by Hilda Conkling

Little Mouse in gray velvet,
Have you had a cheese-breakfast?
There are no crumbs on your coat,
Did you use a napkin?
I wonder what you had to eat,
And who dresses you in gray velvet?

The House
of the Mouse
by Lucy Sprague Mitchell

The house of the mouse
is a wee little house,
a green little house in the grass,
which big clumsy folk
may hunt and may poke
and still never see as they pass
this sweet little, neat little,
wee little, green little,
cuddle-down hide-away
house in the grass.

The Sugar-Plum Tree

by Eugene Field

Have you ever heard of the Sugar-Plum Tree?
    'Tis a marvel of great renown!
It blooms on the shore of the Lollipop Sea
    In the garden of Shut-Eye Town;
The fruit that it bears is so wondrously sweet
    (As those who have tasted it say)
That good little children have only to eat
    Of that fruit to be happy next day.

When you've got to the tree, you would have a hard time
    To capture the fruit which I sing;
The tree is so tall that no person could climb
    To the boughs where the sugar-plums swing!
But up in that tree sits a chocolate cat,
    And a gingerbread dog prowls below—
And this is the way you contrive to get at
    Those sugar-plums tempting you so:

You say but the word to that gingerbread dog
    And he barks with such terrible zest
That the chocolate cat is at once all agog,
    As her swelling proportions attest.
And the chocolate cat goes cavorting around
    From this leafy limb unto that,
And the sugar-plums tumble, of course, to the ground—
    Hurrah for that chocolate cat!

There are marshmallows, gumdrops, and peppermint canes,
    With stripings of scarlet and gold,
And you carry away of the treasure that rains
    As much as your apron can hold!
So come, little child, cuddle closer to me
    In your dainty white nightcap and gown,
And I'll rock you away to that Sugar-Plum Tree
    In the garden of Shut-Eye Town.

Millions of Cats

by Wanda Gág

Once upon a time there was a very old man and a very old woman. They lived in a nice clean house which had flowers all around it, except where the door was. But they couldn't be happy because they were so very lonely.

"If we only had a cat!" sighed the very old woman.

"A cat?" asked the very old man.

"Yes, a sweet little fluffy cat," said the very old woman.

"I will get you a cat, my dear," said the very old man.

And he set out over the hills to look for one. He
climbed over the sunny hills. He trudged through the
cool valleys. He walked a long, long time, and at last he
came to a hill which was quite covered with cats.

Cats here, cats there,
Cats and kittens everywhere,
Hundreds of cats,
Thousands of cats,
Millions and billions and trillions of cats.

"Oh," cried the old man joyfully, "now I can choose
the prettiest cat and take it home with me!" So he chose
one. It was white.

But just as he was about to leave, he saw another one
all black and white, and it seemed just as pretty as the
first. So he took this one also.

But then he saw a fuzzy grey kitten way over here
which was every bit as pretty as the others, so he took it
too.

And now he saw one way down in a corner which he
thought too lovely to leave, so he took this too.

And just then, over here, the very old man found a
kitten which was black and very beautiful.

"It would be a shame to leave that one," said the very
old man. So he took it.

And now, over there, he saw a cat which had brown
and yellow stripes like a baby tiger.

"I simply must take it!" cried the very old man, and
he did.

So it happened that every time the very old man
looked up, he saw another cat which was so pretty he
could not bear to leave it, and before he knew it, he had
chosen them all.

And so he went back over the sunny hills and down
through the cool valleys, to show all his pretty kittens to
the very old woman.

It was very funny to see those hundreds and thousands and
millions and billions and trillions of cats following him.

They came to a pond.

"Mew, mew! We are thirsty!" cried the

Hundreds of cats,
Thousands of cats,
Millions and billions and trillions of cats.

"Well, here is a great deal of water," said the very old man.

Each cat took a sip of water, and the pond was gone!

"Mew, mew! Now we are hungry!" said the

Hundreds of cats,
Thousands of cats,
Millions and billions and trillions of cats.

"There is much grass on the hills," said the very old man.

Each cat ate a mouthful of grass and not a blade was left!

Pretty soon the very old woman saw them coming.

"My dear!" she cried, "What are you doing? I asked for one little cat, and what do I see?—

Cats here, cats there,
Cats and kittens everywhere,
Hundreds of cats,
Thousands of cats,
Millions and billions and trillions of cats.

"But we can never feed them all," said the very old woman. "They will eat us out of house and home."

"I never thought of that," said the very old man. "What shall we do?"

The very old woman thought for a while, and then she said, "I know! We will let the cats decide which one we should keep."

"Oh yes," said the very old man, and he called to the cats, "Which one of you is the prettiest?"

"I am!"

"I am!"

"No, I am!"

"No, I am the prettiest! I am!"

"No, I am! I am! I am!" cried hundreds and thousands and millions and billions and trillions of voices, for each cat thought itself the prettiest.

And they began to quarrel. They bit and scratched

and clawed each other and made such a great noise that the very old man and the very old woman ran into the house as fast as they could. They did not like such quarreling. But after a while the noise stopped and the very old man and the very old woman peeped out of the window to see what had happened. They could not see a single cat!

"I think they must have eaten each other all up," said the very old woman. "It's too bad!"

"But look!" said the very old man, and he pointed to a bunch of high grass. In it sat one little frightened kitten. They went out and picked it up. It was thin and scraggly.

"Poor little kitty," said the very old woman.

"Dear little kitty," said the very old man, "how does it happen that you were not eaten up with all those hundreds and thousands and millions and billions and trillions of cats?"

"Oh, I'm just a very homely little cat," said the kitten, "so when you asked who was the prettiest, I didn't say anything. So nobody bothered about me."

They took the kitten into the house, where the very old woman gave it a warm bath and brushed its fur until it was soft and shiny.

Every day they gave it plenty of milk—and soon it grew nice and plump.

"And it is a very pretty cat, after all!" said the very old woman.

"It is the most beautiful cat in the whole world," said the very old man. "I ought to know, for I've seen—

Hundreds of cats,
Thousands of cats,
Millions and billions and trillions of cats—

and not one was as pretty as this one."

Another fine book by Wanda Gág is *Nothing-at-All*, the story of three little dogs, Pointy, Curly, and an invisible one called Nothing-at-All. And if you think too many pets can be a problem, read *Too Many Rabbits* by Peggy Parish and find out what happens when Miss Molly takes in a stray rabbit just for the night.

The Owl and the Pussycat

by Edward Lear

The Owl and the Pussycat went to sea
In a beautiful pea-green boat,
They took some honey, and plenty of money,
Wrapped up in a five-pound note.
The Owl looked up to the stars above,
And sang to a small guitar,
"O lovely Pussy! O Pussy, my love,
What a beautiful Pussy you are,
You are,
You are!
What a beautiful Pussy you are!"

Pussy said to the Owl, "You elegant fowl!
How charmingly sweet you sing!
O let us be married! too long we have tarried:
But what shall we do for a ring?"
They sailed away for a year and a day,
To the land where the Bong-tree grows;
And there in a wood a Piggy-wig stood,
With a ring at the end of his nose,
His nose,
His nose,
With a ring at the end of his nose.

"Dear Pig, are you willing to sell for one shilling
   Your ring?" Said the Piggy, "I will."
So they took it away, and were married next day
   By the Turkey who lives on the hill.
They dined on mince, and slices of quince,
   Which they ate with a runcible spoon;
And hand in hand, on the edge of the sand,
   They danced by the light of the moon,
         The moon,
         The moon,
   They danced by the light of the moon.

A Kitten
by Eleanor Farjeon

He's nothing much but fur
And two round eyes of blue,
He has a giant purr
And a midget mew.

He darts and pats the air,
He starts and cocks his ear,
When there is nothing there
For him to see and hear.

He runs around in rings,
But why we cannot tell;
With sideways leaps he springs
At things invisible—

Then halfway through a leap
His startled eyeballs close,
And he drops off to sleep
With one paw on his nose.

Little Pussy
by Jane Taylor

I love little pussy,
   Her coat is so warm,
And if I don't hurt her,
   She'll do me no harm.
So I'll not pull her tail,
   Nor drive her away,
But pussy and I
   Very gently will play.

The Bad Kittens
by Elizabeth Coatsworth

You may call, you may call,
But the little black cats won't hear you,
The little black cats are maddened
By the bright green light of the moon,
They are whirling and running and hiding,
They are wild who were once so confiding,
They are crazed when the moon is riding—
You will not catch the kittens soon.
They care not for saucers of milk,
They think not of pillows of silk,
Your softest, crooningest call
Is less than the buzzing of flies.
They are seeing more than you see,
They are hearing more than you hear,
And out of the darkness they peer
With a goblin light in their eyes.

Night
by Lois Weakley McKay

My kitten walks on velvet feet
And makes no sound at all;
And in the doorway nightly sits
To watch the darkness fall.

I think he loves the lady, Night,
And feels akin to her
Whose footsteps are as still as his,
Whose touch as soft as fur.

How the Camel Got His Hump

from *Just So Stories*
by Rudyard Kipling

In the beginning of years, when the world was so new
and all, and the Animals were just beginning to work
for Man, there was a Camel, and he lived in the middle
of a Howling Desert because he did not want to work;
and besides, he was a Howler himself. So he ate sticks
and thorns and tamarisks and milkweed and prickles,
most 'scruciating idle; and when anybody spoke to him
he said "Humph!" Just "Humph!" and no more.

Presently the Horse came to him on Monday morning,
with a saddle on his back and a bit in his mouth, and
said,

"Camel, O Camel, come out and trot like the rest of
us."

"Humph!" said the Camel; and the Horse went away
and told the Man.

Presently the Dog came to him, with a stick in his
mouth, and said, "Camel, O Camel, come and fetch and
carry like the rest of us."

"Humph!" said the Camel; and the Dog went away
and told the Man.

Presently the Ox came to him, with the yoke on his

neck and said, "Camel, O Camel, come and plow like the rest of us."

"Humph!" said the Camel; and the Ox went away and told the Man.

At the end of the day the Man called the Horse and the Dog and the Ox together, and said, "Three, O Three, I'm very sorry for you (with the world so new-and-all); but that Humph-thing in the Desert can't work, or he would have been here by now, so I am going to leave him alone, and you must work double time to make up for it."

That made the Three very angry (with the world so new-and-all), and they held a palaver, and an *indaba*, and a *punchayet*, and a pow-wow on the edge of the Desert; and the Camel came chewing milkweed *most* 'scruciating idle, and laughed at them. Then he said "Humph!" and went away again.

Presently there came along the Djinn in charge of All Deserts, rolling in a cloud of dust (Djinns always travel that way because it is Magic), and he stopped to palaver and pow-wow with the Three.

"Djinn of All Deserts," said the Horse, "*is* it right for any one to be idle, with the world so new-and-all?"

"Certainly not," said the Djinn.

"Well," said the Horse, "there's a thing in the middle of your Howling Desert (and he's a Howler himself) with a long neck and long legs, and he hasn't done a stroke of work since Monday morning. He won't trot."

"Whew!" said the Djinn, whistling, "that's my Camel, for all the gold in Arabia! What does he say about it?"

"He says, 'Humph!' " said the Dog; "and he won't fetch and carry."

"Does he say anything else?"

"Only 'Humph!'; and he won't plow," said the Ox.

"Very good," said the Djinn. "I'll humph him if you will kindly wait a minute."

The Djinn rolled himself up in his dust-cloak, and took a bearing across the desert, and found the Camel most 'scruciatingly idle, looking at his own reflection in a pool of water.

"My long and bubbling friend," said the Djinn, "what's this I hear of your doing no work, with the world so new-and-all?"

"Humph!" said the Camel.

The Djinn sat down, with his chin in his hand, and began to think a Great Magic, while the Camel looked at his own reflection in the pool of water.

"You've given the Three extra work ever since Monday morning, all on account of your 'scruciating idleness," said the Djinn; and he went on thinking Magics, with his chin in his hand.

"Humph!" said the Camel.

"I shouldn't say that again if I were you," said the Djinn; "you might say it once too often. Bubbles, I want you to work."

And the Camel said, "Humph!" again; but no sooner had he said it than he saw his back, that he was so proud of, puffing up and puffing up into a great big lolloping humph.

"Do you see that?" said the Djinn. "That's your very

own humph that you've brought upon your very own self by not working. To-day is Thursday, and you've done no work since Monday, when the work began. Now you are going to work."

"How can I," said the Camel, "with this humph on my back?"

"That's made a-purpose," said the Djinn, "all because you missed those three days. You will be able to work now for three days without eating, because you can live on your humph; and don't you ever say I never did anything for you. Come out of the Desert and go to the Three, and behave. Humph yourself!"

And the Camel humphed himself, humph and all, and went away to join the Three. And from that day to this the Camel always wears a humph (we call it "hump" now, not to hurt his feelings); but he has never yet caught up with the three days he missed at the beginning of the world, and he has never yet learned how to behave.

Rudyard Kipling's book, *Just So Stories*, has many other wonderful tales of how things came to be. Among the best are "How the Leopard Got His Spots" and "The Elephant's Child," which tells how the elephant got its trunk.

The Tale of Custard the Dragon

by Ogden Nash

Belinda lived in a little white house,
With a little black kitten and a little gray mouse,
And a little yellow dog and a little red wagon,
And a realio, trulio, little pet dragon.

Now the name of the little black kitten was Ink,
And the little gray mouse, she called her Blink,
And the little yellow dog was sharp as Mustard,
But the dragon was a coward, and she called him Custard.

Custard the dragon had big sharp teeth,
And spikes on top of him and scales underneath,
Mouth like a fireplace, chimney for a nose,
And realio, trulio daggers on his toes.

Belinda was as brave as a barrel full of bears,
And Ink and Blink chased lions down the stairs,
Mustard was as brave as a tiger in a rage,
But Custard cried for a nice safe cage.

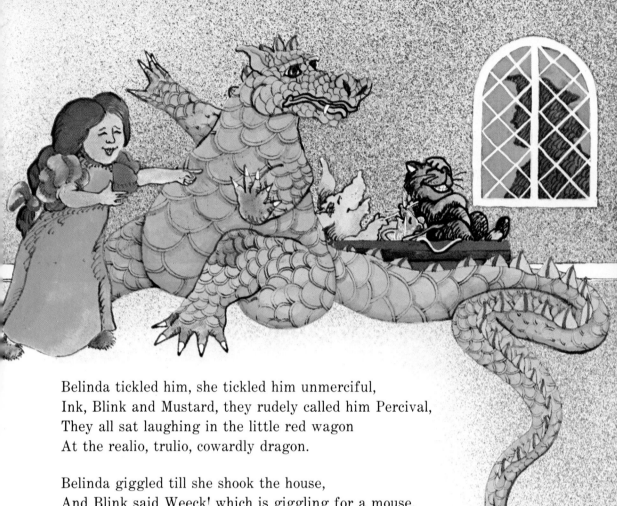

Belinda tickled him, she tickled him unmerciful,
Ink, Blink and Mustard, they rudely called him Percival,
They all sat laughing in the little red wagon
At the realio, trulio, cowardly dragon.

Belinda giggled till she shook the house,
And Blink said Weeck! which is giggling for a mouse,
Ink and Mustard rudely asked his age,
When Custard cried for a nice safe cage.

Suddenly, suddenly they heard a nasty sound,
And Mustard growled, and they all looked around.
Meowch! cried Ink, and Ooh! cried Belinda,
For there was a pirate, climbing in the winda.

Pistol in his left hand, pistol in his right,
And he held in his teeth a cutlass bright,
His beard was black, one leg was wood;
It was clear that the pirate meant no good.

Belinda paled, and she cried Help! Help!
But Mustard fled with a terrified yelp,
Ink trickled down to the bottom of the household,
And little mouse Blink strategically mouseholed.

But up jumped Custard, snorting like an engine,
Clashed his tail like irons in a dungeon,
With a clatter and a clank and a jangling squirm
He went at the pirate like a robin at a worm.

The pirate gaped at Belinda's dragon,
And gulped some grog from his pocket flagon,
He fired two bullets, but they didn't hit,
And Custard gobbled him, every bit.

Belinda embraced him, Mustard licked him,
No one mourned for his pirate victim.
Ink and Blink in glee did gyrate
Around the dragon that ate the pyrate.

But presently up spoke little dog Mustard,
I'd have been twice as brave if I hadn't been flustered.
And up spoke Ink and up spoke Blink,
We'd have been three times as brave, we think,
And Custard said, I quite agree
That everybody is braver than me.

Belinda still lives in her little white house,
With her little black kitten and her little gray mouse,
And her little yellow dog and her little red wagon,
And her realio, trulio, little pet dragon.

Belinda is as brave as a barrel full of bears,
And Ink and Blink chase lions down the stairs.
Mustard is as brave as a tiger in a rage,
But Custard keeps crying for a nice safe cage.

Come Away! Come Away!

from *Peter Pan*
by J. M. Barrie

Peter Pan, the little boy who never grew up, has
been secretly listening to Mrs. Darling tell bedtime
stories to her three children. But one night, when she
shuts the window, she cuts off Peter's shadow. The
next night Mr. and Mrs. Darling go out, leaving the
children in the care of Liza, a servant, and Nana,
their big Newfoundland dog. Peter takes advantage
of this opportunity to return and look for his shadow.

⚜ ⚜ ⚜

For a moment after Mr. and Mrs. Darling left the house
the night-lights by the beds of the three children
continued to burn clearly. They were awfully nice little
night-lights, and one cannot help wishing that they could
have kept awake to see Peter; but Wendy's light blinked
and gave such a yawn that the other two yawned also,
and before they could close their mouths all the three
went out.

There was another light in the room now, a thousand
times brighter than the night-lights, and in the time we
have taken to say this, it has been in all the drawers in
the nursery, looking for Peter's shadow, rummaged the
wardrobe and turned every pocket inside out. It was not

really a light; it made this light by flashing about so
quickly, but when it came to rest for a second you saw it
was a fairy, no longer than your hand, but still growing.
It was a girl called Tinker Bell exquisitely gowned in a
skeleton leaf, cut low and square, through which her
figure could be seen to the best advantage. She was
slightly inclined to *embonpoint*.[1]

A moment after the fairy's entrance the window was
blown open by the breathing of the little stars, and
Peter dropped in. He had carried Tinker Bell part of the
way, and his hand was still messy with the fairy dust.

"Tinker Bell," he called softly, after making sure that
the children were asleep, "Tink, where are you?" She
was in a jug for the moment, and liking it extremely;
she had never been in a jug before.

---

1. Embonpoint is a French word that means "plumpness."

"Oh, do come out of that jug, and tell me, do you know where they put my shadow?"

The loveliest tinkle as of golden bells answered him. It is the fairy language. You ordinary children can never hear it, but if you were to hear it you would know that you had heard it once before.

Tink said that the shadow was in the big box. She meant the chest of drawers, and Peter jumped at the drawers, scattering their contents to the floor with both hands, as kings toss ha'pence to the crowd. In a moment he had recovered his shadow, and in his delight he forgot that he had shut Tinker Bell up in the drawer.

If he thought at all, but I don't believe he ever thought, it was that he and his shadow, when brought near each other, would join like drops of water; and when they did not he was appalled. He tried to stick it on with soap from the bathroom, but that also failed. A shudder passed through Peter, and he sat on the floor and cried.

His sobs woke Wendy, and she sat up in bed. She was not alarmed to see a stranger crying on the nursery floor; she was only pleasantly interested.

"Boy," she said courteously, "why are you crying?"

Peter could be exceedingly polite also, having learned the grand manner at fairy ceremonies, and he rose and bowed to her beautifully. She was much pleased, and bowed beautifully to him from the bed.

"What's your name?" he asked.

"Wendy Moira Angela Darling," she replied with some satisfaction. "What is your name?"

"Peter Pan."

She was already sure that he must be Peter, but it did seem a comparatively short name.

"Is that all?"

"Yes," he said rather sharply. He felt for the first time that it was a shortish name.

"I'm so sorry," said Wendy Moira Angela.

"It doesn't matter," Peter gulped.

She asked where he lived.

"Second to the right," said Peter, "and then straight on till morning."

"What a funny address!"

Peter had a sinking. For the first time he felt that perhaps it was a funny address.

"No, it isn't," he said.

"I mean," Wendy said nicely, remembering that she was hostess, "is that what they put on the letters?"

He wished she had not mentioned letters.

"Don't get any letters," he said contemptuously.

"But your mother gets letters?"

"Don't have a mother," he said. Not only had he no mother, but he had not the slightest desire to have one. He thought them very overrated persons. Wendy, however, felt at once that she was in the presence of a tragedy.

"O Peter, no wonder you were crying," she said, and got out of bed and ran to him.

"I wasn't crying about mothers," he said rather

indignantly. "I was crying because I can't get my shadow to stick on. Besides, I wasn't crying."

"It has come off?"

"Yes."

Then Wendy saw the shadow on the floor, looking so draggled, and she was frightfully sorry for Peter. "How awful!" she said, but she could not help smiling when she saw that he had been trying to stick it on with soap. How exactly like a boy!

Fortunately she knew at once what to do. "It must be sewn on," she said, just a little patronisingly.

"What's sewn?" he asked.

"You're dreadfully ignorant."

"No, I'm not."

But she was exulting in his ignorance. "I shall sew it on for you, my little man," she said, though he was as tall as herself; and she got out her housewife,[2] and sewed the shadow on to Peter's foot.

"I daresay it will hurt a little," she warned him.

"Oh, I shan't cry," said Peter, who was already of opinion that he had never cried in his life. And he clenched his teeth and did not cry; and soon his shadow was behaving properly, though still a little creased.

"Perhaps I should have ironed it," Wendy said thoughtfully; but Peter, boylike, was indifferent to

---

2. A housewife is a small case containing needles, thread, and other sewing things.

appearances, and he was now jumping about in the wildest glee. Alas, he had already forgotten that he owed his bliss to Wendy. He thought he had attached the shadow himself. "How clever I am," he crowed rapturously, "oh, the cleverness of me!"

It is humiliating to have to confess that this conceit of Peter was one of his most fascinating qualities. To put it with brutal frankness, there never was a cockier boy.

But for the moment Wendy was shocked. "You conceit," she exclaimed, with frightful sarcasm; "of course I did nothing!"

"You did a little," Peter said carelessly, and continued to dance.

"A little!" she replied with hauteur; "if I am no use I can at least withdraw"; and she sprang in the most dignified way into bed and covered her face with the blankets.

To induce her to look up he pretended to be going away, and when this failed he sat on the end of the bed and tapped her gently with his foot. "Wendy," he said, "don't withdraw. I can't help crowing, Wendy, when I'm pleased with myself." Still she would not look up, though she was listening eagerly. "Wendy," he continued in a voice that no woman has ever yet been able to resist, "Wendy, one girl is more use than twenty boys."

Now Wendy was every inch a woman, though there were not very many inches, and she peeped out of the bedclothes.

"Do you really think so, Peter?"

"Yes, I do."

"I think it's perfectly sweet of you," she declared, "and I'll get up again"; and she sat with him on the side of the bed. She also said she would give him a kiss if he liked, but Peter did not know what she meant, and he held out his hand expectantly.

"Surely you know what a kiss is?" she asked, aghast.

"I shall know when you give it to me," he replied stiffly; and not to hurt his feeling she gave him a thimble.

"Now," said he, "shall I give you a kiss?" and she replied with a slight primness, "If you please." She made herself rather cheap by inclining her face toward him, but he merely dropped an acorn button into her hand; so she slowly returned her face to where it had been before, and said nicely that she would wear his kiss on the chain round her neck. It was lucky that she did

put it on that chain, for it was afterwards to save her life.

When people in our set are introduced, it is customary for them to ask each other's age, and so Wendy, who always liked to do the correct thing, asked Peter how old he was. It was not really a happy question to ask him; it was like an examination paper that asks grammar, when what you want to be asked is Kings of England.

"I don't know," he replied uneasily, "but I am quite young." He really knew nothing about it; he had merely suspicions, but he said at a venture, "Wendy, I ran away the day I was born."

Wendy was quite surprised, but interested; and she indicated in the charming drawing-room manner, by a touch on her night-gown, that he could sit nearer her.

"It was because I heard father and mother," he explained in a low voice, "talking about what I was to be when I became a man." He was extraordinarily agitated now. "I don't want ever to be a man," he said with passion. "I want always to be a little boy and to have fun. So I ran away to Kensington Gardens and lived a long long time among the fairies."

She gave him a look of the most intense admiration, and he thought it was because he had run away, but it was really because he knew fairies. Wendy had lived such a home life that to know fairies struck her as quite delightful. She poured out questions about them, to his surprise, for they were rather a nuisance to him, getting in his way, and so on, and indeed he sometimes had to give them a hiding. Still, he liked them on the whole, and he told her about the beginnings of fairies.

"You see, Wendy, when the first baby laughed for the first time, its laugh broke into a thousand pieces, and they all went skipping about, and that was the beginning of fairies."

Tedious talk this, but being a stay-at-home she liked it.

"And so," he went on good-naturedly, "there ought to be one fairy for every boy and girl."

"Ought to be? Isn't there?"

"No. You see children know such a lot now, they soon don't believe in fairies, and every time a child says, 'I don't believe in fairies,' there is a fairy somewhere that falls down dead."

Really, he thought they had now talked enough about fairies, and it struck him that Tinker Bell was keeping very quiet. "I can't think where she has gone to," he said, rising, and he called Tink by name. Wendy's heart went flutter with a sudden thrill.

"Peter," she cried, clutching him, "you don't mean to tell me that there is a fairy in this room!"

"She was here just now," he said a little impatiently. "You don't hear her, do you?" and they both listened.

"The only sound I hear," said Wendy, "is like a tinkle of bells."

"Well, that's Tink, that's the fairy language. I think I hear her too."

The sound came from the chest of drawers, and Peter made a merry face. No one could ever look quite so merry as Peter, and the loveliest of gurgles was his laugh. He had his first laugh still.

"Wendy," he whispered gleefully, "I do believe I shut her up in the drawer!"

He let poor Tink out of the drawer, and she flew about the nursery screaming with fury. "You shouldn't say such things," Peter retorted. "Of course I'm very sorry, but how could I know you were in the drawer?"

Wendy was not listening to him. "O Peter," she cried, "if she would only stand still and let me see her!"

"They hardly ever stand still," he said, but for one moment Wendy saw the romantic figure come to rest on the cuckoo clock. "O the lovely!" she cried, though Tink's face was still distorted with passion.

"Tink," said Peter amiably, "this lady says she wishes
you were her fairy."

Tinker Bell answered insolently.

"What does she say, Peter?"

He had to translate. "She is not very polite. She says
you are a great ugly girl, and that she is my fairy."

He tried to argue with Tink. "You know you can't be
my fairy, Tink, because I am a gentleman and you are a
lady."

To this Tink replied in these words, "You silly ass,"
and disappeared into the bathroom. "She is quite a
common fairy," Peter explained apologetically; "she is
called Tinker Bell because she mends the pots and
kettles."

They were together in the armchair by this time, and
Wendy plied him with more questions.

"If you don't live in Kensington Gardens now——"

"Sometimes I do still."

"But where do you live mostly now?"

"With the lost boys."

"Who are they?"

"They are the children who fall out of their

perambulators when the nurse is looking the other way. If they are not claimed in seven days they are sent far away to the Neverland to defray expenses. I'm captain."

"What fun it must be!"

"Yes," said cunning Peter, "but we are rather lonely. You see we have no female companionship."

"Are none of the others girls?"

"Oh no; girls, you know, are much too clever to fall out of their prams."

This flattered Wendy immensely. "I think," she said, "it is perfectly lovely the way you talk about girls; John there just despises us."

For reply Peter rose and kicked John out of bed, blankets and all; one kick. This seemed to Wendy rather forward for a first meeting, and she told him with spirit that he was not captain in her house. However, John continued to sleep so placidly on the floor that she allowed him to remain there. "And I know you meant to be kind," she said, relenting, "so you may give me a kiss."

For the moment she had forgotten his ignorance about kisses. "I thought you would want it back," he said a little bitterly, and offered to return her the thimble.

"Oh dear," said the nice Wendy, "I don't mean a kiss, I mean a thimble."

"What's that?"

"It's like this." She kissed him.

"Funny!" said Peter gravely. "Now shall I give you a thimble?"

"If you wish to," said Wendy, keeping her head erect this time.

Peter thimbled her, and almost immediately she screeched. "What is it, Wendy?"

"It was exactly as if someone were pulling my hair."

"That must have been Tink. I never knew her so naughty before."

And indeed Tink was darting about again, using offensive language.

"She says she will do that to you, Wendy, every time I give you a thimble."

"But why?"

"Why, Tink?"

Again Tink replied, "You silly ass." Peter could not understand why, but Wendy understood; and she was just slightly disappointed when he admitted that he came to the nursery window not to see her but to listen to stories.

"You see, I don't know any stories. None of the lost boys know any stories."

"How perfectly awful," Wendy said.

"Do you know," Peter asked, "why swallows build in the eaves of houses? It is to listen to the stories. O Wendy, your mother was telling you such a lovely story."

"Which story was it?"

"About the prince who couldn't find the lady who wore the glass slipper."

"Peter," said Wendy excitedly, "that was Cinderella, and he found her, and they lived happy ever after."

Peter was so glad that he rose from the floor, where they had been sitting, and hurried to the window. "Where are you going?" she cried with misgiving.

"To tell the other boys."

"Don't go, Peter," she entreated, "I know such lots of stories."

Those were her precise words, so there can be no denying that it was she who first tempted him.

He came back, and there was a greedy look in his eyes now which ought to have alarmed her, but did not.

"Oh, the stories I could tell to the boys!" she cried, and then Peter gripped her and began to draw her toward the window.

"Let me go!" she ordered him.

"Wendy, do come with me and tell the other boys."

Of course she was very pleased to be asked, but she said, "Oh dear, I can't. Think of mummy! Besides, I can't fly."

"I'll teach you."

"Oh, how lovely to fly."

"I'll teach you how to jump on the wind's back, and then away we go."

"Oo!" she exclaimed rapturously.

"Wendy, Wendy, when you are sleeping in your silly bed you might be flying about with me saying funny things to the stars."

"Oo!"

"And Wendy, there are mermaids."

"Mermaids! With tails?"

"Such long tails."

"Oh," cried Wendy, "to see a mermaid!"

He had become frightfully cunning. "Wendy," he said, "how we should all respect you."

She was wriggling her body in distress. It was quite as if she were trying to remain on the nursery floor.

But he had no pity for her.

"Wendy," he said, the sly one, "you could tuck us in at night."

"Oo!"

"None of us has even been tucked in at night."

"Oo," and her arms went out to him.

"And you could darn our clothes, and make pockets for us. None of us has any pockets."

How could she resist. "Of course it's awfully fascinating!" she cried. "Peter, would you teach John and Michael to fly too?"

"If you like," he said indifferently; and she ran to John and Michael and shook them. "Wake up," she cried, "Peter Pan has come and he is to teach us to fly."

John rubbed his eyes. "Then I shall get up," he said. Of course he was on the floor already. "Hallo," he said, "I am up!"

Michael was up by this time also, looking as sharp as a knife with six blades and a saw, but Peter suddenly signed silence. Their faces assumed the awful craftiness of children listening for sounds from the grown-up

world. All was as still as salt. Then everything was right. No, stop! Everything was wrong. Nana, who had been barking distressfully all the evening, was quiet now. It was her silence they had heard.

"Out with the light! Hide! Quick!" cried John, taking command for the only time throughout the whole adventure. And thus when Liza entered, holding Nana, the nursery seemed quite its old self, very dark; and you could have sworn you heard its three wicked inmates breathing angelically as they slept. They were really doing it artfully from behind the window curtains.

Liza was in a bad temper, for she was mixing the Christmas puddings in the kitchen, and had been drawn away from them, with a raisin still on her cheek, by Nana's absurd suspicions. She thought the best way of getting a little quiet was to take Nana to the nursery for a moment, but in custody of course.

"There, you suspicious brute," she said, not sorry that Nana was in disgrace, "they are perfectly safe, aren't they? Every one of the little angels sound asleep in bed. Listen to their gentle breathing."

Here Michael, encouraged by his success, breathed so loudly that they were nearly detected. Nana knew that kind of breathing, and she tried to drag herself out of Liza's clutches.

But Liza was dense. "No more of it, Nana," she said sternly, pulling her out of the room. "I warn you if you bark again I shall go straight for master and missus and bring them home from the party, and then, oh, won't master whip you, just."

She tied the unhappy dog up again, but do you think Nana ceased to bark? Bring master and missus home from the party! Why, that was just what she wanted. Do you think she cared whether she was whipped so long as her charges were safe? Unfortunately Liza returned to her puddings, and Nana, seeing that no help would come from her, strained and strained at the chain until at last she broke it. In another moment she had burst into the dining-room of 27 and flung up her paws to heaven, her

most expressive way of making a communication. Mr.
and Mrs. Darling knew at once that something terrible
was happening in their nursery, and without a good-bye
to their hostess they rushed into the street.

But it was now ten minutes since three scoundrels had
been breathing behind the curtains; and Peter Pan can
do a great deal in ten minutes.

We now return to the nursery.

"It's all right," John announced, emerging from his
hiding-place. "I say, Peter, can you really fly?"

Instead of troubling to answer him Peter flew around
the room, taking the mantelpiece on the way.

"How topping!" said John and Michael.

"How sweet!" cried Wendy.

"Yes, I'm sweet, oh, I am sweet!" said Peter,
forgetting his manners again.

It looked delightfully easy, and they tried it first from
the floor and then from the beds, but they always went
down instead of up.

"I say, how do you do it?" asked John, rubbing his
knee. He was quite a practical boy.

"You just think lovely wonderful thoughts," Peter explained, "and they lift you up in the air."

He showed them again.

"You're so nippy at it," John said; "couldn't you do it very slowly once?"

Peter did it both slowly and quickly. "I've got it now, Wendy!" cried John, but soon he found he had not. Not one of them could fly an inch, though even Michael was in words of two syllables, and Peter did not know A from Z.

Of course Peter had been trifling with them, for no one can fly unless the fairy dust has been blown on him. Fortunately, as we have mentioned, one of his hands was messy with it, and he blew some on each of them, with the most superb results.

"Now just wriggle your shoulders this way," he said, "and let go."

They were all on their beds, and gallant Michael let go first. He did not quite mean to let go, but he did it, and immediately he was borne across the room.

"I flewed!" he screamed while still in mid-air.

John let go and met Wendy near the bathroom.

"Oh, lovely!"

"Oh, ripping!"

"Look at me!"

"Look at me!"

"Look at me!"

They were not nearly so elegant as Peter, they could not help kicking a little, but their heads were bobbing against the ceiling, and there is almost nothing so delicious as that. Peter gave Wendy a hand at first, but had to desist, Tink was so indignant.

Up and down they went, and round and round. Heavenly was Wendy's word.

"I say," cried John, "why shouldn't we all go out?"

Of course it was to this that Peter had been luring them.

Michael was ready: he wanted to see how long it took him to do a billion miles. But Wendy hesitated.

"Mermaids!" said Peter again.

"Oo!"

"And there are pirates."

"Pirates," cried John, seizing his Sunday hat, "let us go at once."

It was just at this moment that Mr. and Mrs. Darling hurried with Nana out of 27. They ran into the middle of the street to look up at the nursery window; and, yes, it was still shut, but the room was ablaze with light, and most heart-gripping sight of all, they could see in shadow on the curtain three little figures in night attire circling round and round, not on the floor but in the air.

Not three figures, four!

In a tremble they opened the street door. Mr. Darling would have rushed upstairs, but Mrs. Darling signed to him to go softly. She even tried to make her heart go softly.

Will they reach the nursery in time? If so, how delightful for them, and we shall all breathe a sigh of relief, but there will be no story. On the other hand, if they are not in time, I solemnly promise that it will all come right in the end.

They would have reached the nursery in time had it not been that the little stars were watching them. Once again the stars blew the window open, and that smallest star of all called out:

"Cave,[3] Peter!"

---

3. Cave is British slang for "beware! look out!" It comes from the Latin word *cave*, meaning "beware."

Then Peter knew that there was not a moment to lose. "Come," he cried imperiously, and soared out at once into the night, followed by John and Michael and Wendy.

Mr. and Mrs. Darling and Nana rushed into the nursery too late. The birds were flown.

Peter Pan, Tinker Bell, Wendy, John, and Michael fly off to Neverland, where they have many wonderful adventures—all of which you can share in the complete book. More of Peter's adventures can be found in another book by J. M. Barrie, *Peter Pan in Kensington Gardens*.

I Keep Three Wishes Ready

by Annette Wynne

I keep three wishes ready,
Lest I should chance to meet,
Any day a fairy
Coming down the street.

I'd hate to have to stammer,
Or have to think them out,
For it's very hard to think things up
When a fairy is about.

And I'd hate to lose my wishes,
For fairies fly away,
And perhaps I'd never have a chance
On any other day.

So I keep three wishes ready,
Lest I should chance to meet,
Any day a fairy
Coming down the street.

The Little Elfman

by John Kendrick Bangs

I met a little Elfman once,
    Down where the lilies blow.
I asked him why he was so small,
    And why he didn't grow.

He slightly frowned, and with his eye
    He looked me through and through—
"I'm just as big for me," said he,
    "As you are big for you!"

The Best Game
the Fairies Play

by Rose Fyleman

The best game the fairies play,
    The best game of all,
Is sliding down steeples—
    (You know they're very tall.)
You fly to the weathercock,
    And when you hear it crow
You fold your wings and clutch your things
    And then let go!

They have a million other games—
    Cloud-catching's one,
And mud-mixing after rain
    Is heaps and heaps of fun;
But when you go and stay with them
    Never mind the rest,
Take my advice—they're very nice,
    But steeple-sliding's best!

My Shadow

by Robert Louis Stevenson

I have a little shadow that goes in and out with me,
And what can be the use of him is more than I can see.
He is very, very like me from the heels up to the head;
And I see him jump before me, when I jump into my bed.

The funniest thing about him is the way he likes to grow—
Not at all like proper children, which is always very slow;
For he sometimes shoots up taller like an India-rubber ball,
And he sometimes gets so little that there's none of him at all.

He hasn't got a notion of how children ought to play,
And can only make a fool of me in every sort of way.
He stays so close beside me, he's a coward you can see;
I'd think shame to stick to nursie as that shadow sticks to me!

One morning, very early, before the sun was up,
I rose and found the shining dew on every buttercup;
But my lazy little shadow, like an arrant sleepyhead,
Had stayed at home behind me and was fast asleep in bed.

Wynken, Blynken, and Nod

by Eugene Field

Wynken, Blynken, and Nod one night
  Sailed off in a wooden shoe—
Sailed on a river of crystal light
  Into a sea of dew.
"Where are you going, and what do you wish?"
  The old moon asked the three.
"We have come to fish for the herring fish
  That live in this beautiful sea;
  Nets of silver and gold have we!"
          Said Wynken,
          Blynken,
          And Nod.

The old moon laughed and sang a song,
  As they rocked in the wooden shoe,
And the wind that sped them all night long
  Ruffled the waves of dew.
The little stars were the herring fish
  That lived in that beautiful sea—
"Now cast your nets wherever you wish—
  Never afeard are we!"
  So cried the stars to the fishermen three,
          Wynken,
          Blynken,
          And Nod.

All night long their nets they threw
   To the stars in the twinkling foam—
Then down from the skies came the wooden shoe,
   Bringing the fishermen home;
'Twas all so pretty a sail it seemed
   As if it could not be,
And some folks thought 'twas a dream they'd dreamed
   Of sailing that beautiful sea—
   But I shall name you the fishermen three:
                Wynken,
                Blynken,
                And Nod.

Wynken and Blynken are two little eyes,
   And Nod is a little head,
And the wooden shoe that sailed the skies
   Is a wee one's trundle-bed.
So shut your eyes while mother sings
   Of wonderful sights that be,
And you shall see the beautiful things
   As you rock in the misty sea
   Where the old shoe rocked the fishermen three:
                Wynken,
                Blynken,
                And Nod.

Rosa-Too-Little

by Sue Felt

It was winter. The snow was piled in shapeless mounds
along 110th Street.

But it wasn't the snow that bothered Rosa as she
followed Margarita up the library steps into the warm
indoors.

For as long as she could remember Rosa had been
following her big sister, Margarita, to the library.

And every time Rosa waited while Margarita returned
her books.

And every time she waited Rosa was sad. She wanted
very much to have books of her own to return.

"Please, Margarita," she would say, "when can I join?"

"You are too little, Rosa. You have to write your name
and get a card before you can take books out."

"It is always the same. Last winter I was too little. Last summer I was too little. Why am I always too little to have my own books?" Rosa sighed.

Rosa was big enough to help her mother at home while Margarita and Antonio were at school. But whenever Margarita came from school to take her to the library, Rosa was ready.

Always before Margarita chose new books she would hold Rosa up to press her face against the cool glass to look into that small other world of the Peep Show.

"Oh, there is Peter Rabbit in bed," Rosa would say, "and there is Mrs. Rabbit making him some Camomile Tea and Flopsy, Mopsy, and Cottontail are eating bread and milk and blackberries."

On Fridays Margarita and Antonio went to Story Hour upstairs while Rosa, who was too little, sat in the Reading Room looking at Picture Books. She looked at the pictures until she knew every one by heart. This made Rosa sad, too. She was certain that if she could only have her own library card and take home her own books she would be able to read them. She wanted so much to go to Story Hour, too, and hear the library teacher tell fairy tales. Sometimes Margarita told Rosa the stories or read them to her at home. But Rosa knew it was not quite the same as hearing them at Story Hour. She was sure she must be nearly big enough to make a wish and help blow out the candle after Story Hour. Antonio had told her about that part, too.

"Oh, how I would like to do that. Why am I always too little?" Rosa sighed.

The snow melted. After light spring rains the trees in Central Park were fringed with baby green leaves.

Margarita carried her jump rope to school and often played double Dutch on the sidewalks in the evenings as the nights grew warmer.

And Rosa was too little for jump rope.

When Margarita wasn't jumping rope she was roller skating. And Mother said Rosa was too little for roller skates.

It seemed to Rosa she was too little for anything. Antonio and his friends once again were training their pigeons on the rooftops. Antonio and his friends didn't want her on the roof. And Antonio was too busy to take her to the library. No one would take her to the library. And that was what Rosa wanted to do most of all.

She was sad.

Rosa begged and begged her mother to let her go alone to the library.

Finally one day her mother said yes.

Rosa could go all by herself. She remembered to wait for the green lights crossing the street. She remembered to wait in line. She was very proud to do it all alone.

But when at last she reached the desk and the library teacher asked for her books, Rosa suddenly remembered something else.

Rosa Maldonado did not have any books; she did not even have a library card. She was too little to join. Poor little Rosa covered her face, pushed her way out of the line, and ran down the stairs, out the door, and all the way home.

"Rosa, little dear, what is the matter, *chiquita?*" her mother asked. Rosa sobbed louder, but at last her mother understood.

"Rosa," she comforted, "we will make a plan, a secret for you and me!"

And Rosa was not quite so sad!

The next day was hot, but Rosa and her mother didn't mind. They started their plan.

All through the long, hot, city summer Rosa worked on her plan except for the days when the street-cleaning men turned on the water hydrant, *the Pompa*, Rosa, Margarita, and Antonio called it. Then they rushed through the fast, cold spray of water. The pavement was cool on the soles of their feet.

Most of the children forgot about books, but not Rosa.

Sometimes in the afternoon Margarita took Rosa to hear the Picture Books read in the library. Everything was quiet in the summer. There were not so many children, for some of them were in camp and some were in the country and all the rest were too hot and sticky to do much of anything.

Rosa listened to the stories and smiled inside with her secret.

And every day Rosa worked on her plan in a special corner at home so that Margarita and Antonio wouldn't guess.

One day Mama said:

"When school starts in September, Rosa may go with Margarita and Antonio."

Then Rosa smiled. She was not too little any more. She could hardly wait.

The last day before school was to begin the little penny merry-go-round came. *La machina,* the children called it. Everyone on 110th Street who had pennies had a ride, and the others followed the music. But they weren't so happy as when *la machina* had been there in the spring. Playtime was over—no more long days of jump rope, marbles, skating, and stoopball.

But Rosa skipped with joy.

On Monday school started, and Rosa walked with Margarita and Antonio—quiet and proud. It was very exciting to be in school, but there was something else Rosa wanted to do, too.

At three o'clock she waited by the playground gate till Margarita and Antonio came out and then Rosa pulled her sister's hand.

"Margarita, Margarita, today may I go?"

"Rosa, what are you talking about? How do you like school?" said Margarita.

"It's wonderful. But Margarita, today may I go to the library with you?" asked Rosa, still pulling her sister's hand.

"But Rosa," said Margarita, "why today? I have homework to do."

"Please, Margarita." And finally Margarita gave in to Rosa's pleading and they went together to the library.

Lots of boys and girls were back again to get their cards after the summer. Soon Rosa's turn came.

"What do you want, Rosa?" asked the librarian, who had seen Rosa so many times she knew her name.

"I want to join, please," said Rosa.

"Oh, but Rosa, you are very little. You must be able to write your name, you know."

"I can write my name," Rosa said proudly.

The library lady smiled and took a white slip of paper

from a drawer, dipped a pen in the inkwell, and said: "Write your name on this line, Rosa."

Rosa held tight to the pen and carefully, carefully made the letters.

The pen scratched. Rosa wasn't used to ink, and she wasn't sure the librarian could read her name, but when Rosa looked up, the library lady smiled.

"That's fine, Rosa," she said.

"Why, Rosa," Margarita said, "that's wonderful!" and she wrote in the address and school and Rosa's grade and age.

"Rosa, take this home and have your mother fill out the other side, then bring it back," the librarian said.

Rosa ran down the stairs and out the door. She ran all the way home and into the kitchen where her mother was preparing dinner.

"Mama, Mama, I joined, I joined! I wrote my name and you must sign the paper so I can get my card."

Her mother smiled proudly and kissed Rosa's hot little face. She signed her name and Rosa's father's name on the back of the paper.

The librarian was surprised to see Rosa back so soon.

"I ran," Rosa said, and showed her mother's name on the paper. Then the librarian gave Rosa a blue slip of paper and Rosa wrote her name again. All the time Rosa saw her name on a brand-new card. It would be all her own. The library teacher helped her read the pledge:

> When I write my name in this book, I promise to take good care of the books I use in the library and at home and to obey the rules of the library.

Then Rosa stood on a stool and wrote her name in the big book. That was the best moment of all, because now Rosa Maldonado's name was in the book, the big black book where all the other children who could write had signed their names.

She listened to the rules carefully, although she already knew them. She promised to take good care of

her books and to bring them back on time and always to have her hands clean!

Then Rosa walked over to the Easy Books and found the two books she wanted. She knew just where to find them.

Rosa then waited in line to have her books stamped. She smiled back at the library teacher. Then she walked down the library stairs and out into the brisk evening. She squeezed her very own books.

"I am not too little any more," said Rosa.

She was very happy.

Tell Me Some More by Crosby Bonsall and *Mike's House* by Julia Sauer are two other good stories about children and libraries. And if you want to meet another delightful Puerto Rican family, try *Friday Night Is Papa Night* by Ruth Sonneborn.

Thaw
by Eunice Tietjens

The snow is soft,
    and how it squashes!
"Galumph, galumph!"
    go my galoshes.

The Mitten Song
(*to be chanted*)
by Marie Louise Allen

"Thumbs in the thumb-place,
Fingers all together!"
This is the song
We sing in mitten-weather.
When it is cold,
It doesn't matter whether
Mittens are wool,
Or made of finest leather.
This is the song
We sing in mitten-weather:
"Thumbs in the thumb-place,
Fingers all together!"

My Zipper Suit
by Marie Louise Allen

My zipper suit is bunny-brown—
The top zips up, the legs zip down.
I wear it every day.
My daddy brought it out from town.
Zip it up, and zip it down,
And hurry out to play!

288

Cynthia in the Snow

by Gwendolyn Brooks

IT SUSHES.
It hushes
The loudness in the road.
It flitter-twitters,
And laughs away from me.
It laughs a lovely whiteness,
And whitely whirs away,
To be
Some otherwhere,
Still white as milk or shirts.
So beautiful it hurts.

City Lights

by Rachel Field

Into the endless dark
The lights of the buildings shine,
Row upon twinkling row,
Line upon glistening line.
Up and up they mount
Till the tallest seems to be
The topmost taper set
On a towering Christmas tree.

City

by Langston Hughes

In the morning the city
Spreads its wings
Making a song
In stone that sings.

In the evening the city
Goes to bed
Hanging lights
About its head.

290

Snowy Morning
by Lilian Moore

Wake
gently this morning
to a different day.
Listen.
There is no bray
of buses,
no brake growls,
no siren howls and
no horns
blow.
There is only
the silence
of a city
hushed
by snow.

Ice
by Dorothy Aldis

When it is the winter time
    I run up the street
And I make the ice laugh
    With my little feet—
"Crickle, crackle, crickle
    Crrreeet, crrreeet, crrreeet."

Things to Know

An Animal Alphabet

Aa

A is for ant.
Where there's one, there are many.
You either see lots
or you don't see any.

Bb

B is for bear
asleep in its den.
When spring comes around
it will wake up again.

Cc

C is for cat,
so soft and so furry,
dainty and curious,
mewy and purry.

Dd

D is for dog
with a cold, wet nose,
who follows its master
wherever he goes.

Ee

E is for eagle
that soars through the air
and hunts from the sky
when the weather is fair.

293

Ff

F is for fly
that makes a loud buzz
whenever it flies—
which it often does.

Gg

G is for goat
on a mountain high,
grazing on grass
while the clouds roll by.

Hh

H is for horse,
whose feet go clup-clup.
It can run like the wind,
and it sleeps standing up.

Ii

I is for iguana.

A dragon it's not.
It's a sun-loving lizard
that lives where it's hot.

Jj

J is for jay,

a bird far from quiet.
Three jays in a tree
are a fine-feathered riot!

Kk

K is for koala.

It looks like a bear,
but it eats eucalyptus,
and bears wouldn't dare.

Ll

L is for lion,
who lies in the sun
and never eats lunch
on a hamburger bun.

Mm

M is for mouse,
a tiny, shy beast
that is clever at finding
its way to a feast.

Nn

N is for narwhal
that swims all about—
a small kind of whale
with a horn on its snout.

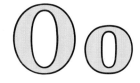

Oo

O is for otter,
who often eats
(without any lemon)
fishy treats.

Pp

P is for penguin,
a bird that won't freeze
when it swims like a fish
in icy-cold seas.

Q q

Q is for quail,
who is hard to see
when standing in dry leaves,
quietly.

Rr

R is for robin
with a cheery red breast,
who lays her blue eggs
in a shaggy brown nest.

Ss

S is for snail
with its house on its back,
who slides slowly along
on a slippery track.

Tt

T is for toad,
and also for treat.
A treat for a toad
is a bug to eat!

Uu

U is for unicorn,
a fairy-tale horse
with a horn on its head.
That's magic, of course!

V is for vulture

that feeds on things dead.
(It would probably rather
eat pancakes instead!)

W is for worm

that eats dirt for dinner.
If that's what we ate,
We'd all be much thinner!

X as in fox

that hunts in the night
and can hear any noise,
no matter how slight.

Y is for yak,

with its shaggy, thick hair.
It lives high in the mountains,
and it's c-cold up there!

Z is for zebra,

It's black, striped with white—
or else white with black stripes—
I'm not sure which is right.

Number Rhymes from Mother Goose

One to Make Ready

One to make ready,
And two to prepare;
Good luck to the rider,
And away goes the mare.

One for the Money

One for the money,
And two for the show,
Three to make ready,
And four to go.

One for Anger

One for anger,
Two for mirth,
Three for a wedding,
Four for a birth,
Five for rich,
Six for poor,
Seven for a witch,
I can tell you no more.

1, 2, 3, 4

1, 2, 3, 4,
Mary at the cottage door
5, 6, 7, 8,
Eating cherries off a plate.

1, 2, 3, 4, 5!

1, 2, 3, 4, 5!
I caught a hare alive;
6, 7, 8, 9, 10!
I let her go again.

Seven Blackbirds
in a Tree

Seven blackbirds in a tree,
Count them and see what they be.
One for sorrow
Two for joy
Three for a girl
Four for a boy
Five for silver
Six for gold
Seven for a secret
That's never been told.

One, Two,
Buckle My Shoe

One, two,
Buckle my shoe;

Three, four,
Knock at the door;

Five, six,
Pick up sticks;

Seven, eight,
Lay them straight;

Nine, ten,
A big fat hen.

Days of the Week from Mother Goose

Monday's Child

Monday's child is fair of face,
Tuesday's child is full of grace,
Wednesday's child is full of woe,
Thursday's child has far to go,
Friday's child is loving and giving,
Saturday's child works hard for his living,
And the child that is born on the Sabbath day
Is bonny and blithe and good and gay.

Wash on Monday

Wash on Monday,
Iron on Tuesday,
Mend on Wednesday
Churn on Thursday,
Clean on Friday,
Bake on Saturday,
Rest on Sunday.

Solomon Grundy

Solomon Grundy,
Born on a Monday,
Christened on Tuesday,
Married on Wednesday,
Took ill on Thursday,
Worse on Friday,
Died on Saturday,
Buried on Sunday.
This is the end
Of Solomon Grundy.

Months of the Year

January

The Garden Year
by Sara Coleridge

January brings the snow,
Makes our feet and fingers glow.

February brings the rain,
Thaws the frozen lake again.

March brings breezes, loud and shrill,
To stir the dancing daffodil.

April brings the primrose sweet,
Scatters daisies at our feet.

April

May brings flocks of pretty lambs
Skipping by their fleecy dams.

June brings tulips, lilies, roses,
Fills the children's hands with posies.

Hot July brings cooling showers,
Apricots, and gillyflowers.

July

August brings the sheaves of corn;
Then the harvest home is borne.

Warm September brings the fruit;
Sportsmen then begin to shoot.

Fresh October brings the pheasant;
Then to gather nuts is pleasant.

October

Dull November brings the blast;
Then the leaves are whirling fast.

Chill December brings the sleet,
Blazing fire, and Christmas treat.

February

March

May

June

August

September

November

December

How Many Colors?

What Is Pink?

by Christina Rossetti

What is pink? a rose is pink
By the fountain's brink.
What is red? a poppy's red
In its barley bed.
What is blue? the sky is blue
Where the clouds float thro'.
What is white? a swan is white
Sailing in the light.
What is yellow? pears are yellow,
Rich and ripe and mellow.
What is green? the grass is green,
With small flowers between.
What is violet? clouds are violet
In the summer twilight.
What is orange? why, an orange,
Just an orange!

The Purple Cow
by Gelett Burgess

I never saw a Purple Cow,
  I never hope to see one,
But I can tell you, anyhow,
  I'd rather see than be one!

Yellow
by David McCord

Green is go,
and red is stop,
and yellow is peaches
with cream on top.

Earth is brown,
and blue is sky;
yellow looks well
on a butterfly.

Clouds are white,
black, pink, or mocha;
yellow's a dish of
tapioca.

309

Time Rhymes from Mother Goose

Hickory, Dickory, Dock

Hickory, dickory, dock,
The mouse ran up the clock.
   The clock struck one,
   The mouse ran down,
Hickory, dickory, dock.

Bell Horses

Bell horses, bell horses,
   What time of day?
One o'clock, two o'clock,
   Three and away.

A Diller, a Dollar

A diller, a dollar,
A ten o'clock scholar!
What makes you come so soon?
You used to come at ten o'clock,
But now you come at noon.

The Clock

Tick, tock, tick, tock,
Merrily sings the clock;
   It's time for work,
   It's time for play,
So it sings throughout the day.
Tick, tock, tick, tock,
Merrily sings the clock.

Illustration
Acknowledgments

The publishers of *Childcraft* gratefully acknowledge
the following artists, photographers, publishers,
agencies, and corporations for illustrations in this
volume. Page numbers refer to two-page spreads.
All illustrations are the exclusive property of the
publishers of *Childcraft* unless names are marked
with an asterisk (*).

10-11: Kinuko Craft	75: Jan Palmer	207: Robert Byrd
13-19: Jan Brett	76-86: Robert Byrd	208-209: Linda Liefer
20-21: Kinuko Craft	87-89: Cindy S. Rosenheim	210: Robert Byrd
23: Uri Shulevitz	90-94: Jan Brett	211-215: Ron Brooks*
24-25: Ron LeHew	95-101: Linda Liefer	216-217: Robert Byrd
26: Linda Gist	102-109: Yoshi Miyake	218-233: Dennis Hockerman
27: Kinuko Craft	110-116: Jan Brett	234-235: Garth Williams
28: Ron LeHew	117-125: Jerry Pinkney	237: Susan Lexa
29: Linda Gist	126-137: Susan Lexa	238-243: Robert Byrd
30-31: Christine Westerberg	138-139: Yoshi Miyake	244-245: Ron LeHew
32-33: Ron LeHew	140-141: Robert Byrd	246-247: Susan Lexa
34-35: Lucinda McQueen	142-143: Linda Liefer	248-251: Yoshi Miyake
36-37: Jan Brett	144-145: Robert Byrd	252-255: Laurie Hamilton
38-43: Kinuko Craft	146-153: Jerry Pinkney	256-275: Jan Palmer
44-45: Lucinda McQueen	154-161: Yoshi Miyake	276: Linda Liefer
46-47: Susan Lexa	162-163: Susan Lexa	277: Tom di Grazia
48-49: Ron LeHew	164: Robert Byrd	278-279: Susan Lexa
50-51: Kinuko Craft	165-168: Ezra Jack Keats*	280-287: Lucinda McQueen
52-53: Jan Brett	169: Robert Byrd	288-291: Dennis Hockerman
54-57: Ron LeHew	170-171: Jan Palmer	292-301: Diane Paterson
58-59: Linda Liefer	172-176: Beatrix Potter*	302-304: Nan Brooks
60-63: Lucinda McQueen	177: Linda Liefer	305: Diane Paterson
64-68: Kinuko Craft	178-179: Robert Byrd	306-309: Nan Brooks
69-71: Linda Liefer	180-187: E. H. Shephard*	310-311: Diane Paterson
72-73: Jan Palmer	188-191: Susan Lexa	
74: Kinuko Craft	192-206: Linda Liefer	Cover: Yoshi Miyake

Author Index

This index is divided into two parts: **Authors of Stories** and **Authors of Poems**. If you know the name of the author you are looking for, use this index. You can also find a story or a poem by using the **Title Index** on page 315, or the **Subject Index** on page 319, or a poem by using the **First-Line Index** on page 318. For more stories and poems, see the indexes in volumes 2 and 3. For stories and poems in all other volumes, see the entries **poems and rhymes, poets,** and **stories** in the General Index in Volume 15.

Title Index

This index is divided into two parts: **Titles of Stories** and **Titles of Poems**. If you know the title of the story or poem you are looking for, use this index. You can also find a story or a poem by using the **Author Index** on page 313 or the **Subject Index** on page 319, or a poem by using the **First-Line Index** on page 318. For more stories and poems, see the indexes in volumes 2 and 3. For stories and poems in all other volumes, see the entries **poems and rhymes, poets,** and **stories** in the General Index in Volume 15.

First-Line Index to Poems

Use this index to find a poem if you know only the first line of the poem. You can also find a poem by using the **Author Index** on page 313, the **Title Index** on page 315, or the **Subject Index** on page 318. For more poems, see the indexes in volumes 2 and 3. For poems in all other volumes, see the entries **poems and rhymes** and **poets** in the General Index in Volume 15.

Subject Index

Use this index to find a story or poem about a particular
subject. You can also find a story or poem by using the **Author
Index** on page 313 or the **Title Index** on page 315, or a poem
by using the **First-Line Index** on page 317. For more stories
and poems, see the indexes in volumes 2 and 3. For stories
and poems in all other volumes, see the entries **poems and
rhymes, poets,** and **stories** in the General Index in Volume 15.